Penguins
Seals, Dolphins, Salmon and Eels

D1610204

Karl König

Penguins
Seals, Dolphins, Salmon and Eels

Sketches for an Imaginative Zoology

Floris Books

First published in German as essays
in *Die Drei* between 1956 and 1966.
First published in volume form as *Bruder Tier*
by Verlag Freies Geistesleben, Stuttgart, 1967.

This volume, consisting of four of the eleven essays
in *Bruder Tier*, first published in English in 1984.

'The Origin of Seals' and 'The Life of Penguins' were
translated by Richard Aylward.
'The Migrations of Salmon and Eels' was first published in
English in the *British Homoeopathic Journal*, July 1962.
'Dolphins — Children of the Sea' was first published in the
Golden Blade 1967.

© 1967 Verlag Freies Geistesleben GmbH Stuttgart.
This translation © Floris Books 1984.
All rights reserved. No part of this publication may be
reproduced without the prior permission of Floris Books,
21 Napier Road, Edinburgh.

British Library Cataloguing in Publication Data

Konig, Karl
Penguins, seals, dolphins, salmon and eels.
1. Vertebrates   2. Marine fauna
I. Title   II. Bruder Tier. *English*
596.092   QL605

ISBN 0–86315–014–4

Printed in Great Britain
by Billing & Sons Ltd, Worcester

Contents

References

The system used in this book quotes author and year of publication, followed by volume (if necessary) and page. The full title and publication details are in the bibliography. References to lectures by Rudolf Steiner include the date of the lecture in square brackets.

Foreword

In 1928 Karl König came to London to take part in a conference together with other followers of the spiritual teacher Rudolf Steiner. It was typical of this twenty-six-year-old Viennese doctor that he should make time on his first visit to have a look round the squalid East End of the city. He poured out his heart to Friedrich Rittelmeyer, father figure and founder of The Christian Community, about the misery and suffering he felt crying out for help in the slums. But König not only had a capacity for compassion but a flair for dynamic leadership, enabling him to put into practice his ideals for forming a community life that would include the deprived. When, ten years later, an empty manse on an estate in Scotland was made available to him it became the first base for his work with children and others needing the special care and attention of a devoted community to live in. This work developed by leaps and bounds until the Camphill community has become a veritable empire, receiving considerable state subsidies in recognition of its important role in society.

As a lecturer and occasional writer, Karl König was clearly indebted to Anthroposophy, taught by Rudolf Steiner, but he also has a unique spiritual 'eye' of his own. He was filled with brotherly kinship not only towards the human being in need, but also towards the animals. During the last ten years of his life, he worked intermittently on a series of what eventually became eleven essays about animals. These were put together after his death in 1966 under the title *Bruder Tier* (Brother Animal). For this first English edition, to be published in three separate volumes, only very small revisions have been made. Despite the passing of time, we have here real treasure. Nothing quite comparable on animals is to be found anywhere else. The fairly heady insights of Anthroposophy, the mythological archetypes, the scientific wonders are all infused with much compassion and understanding for the true being of animals. Karl König seems to get right inside their skins (scales, fur or feathers) and experience from there new horizons of consciousness. I feel sure he would still love them as his brothers even if they had not been, as he so deftly portrayed, of such vital importance for human life and the continued evolution of the earth.

Michael Jones

The Origin of Seals

1 Migration of animals

A constant urge to migrate pervades the entire animal kingdom. There is hardly a family or a species for which migrating and returning are not an integral part of existence. The journeys may be long or short. Certain species cross oceans; others fly over entire continents.

This migration occurs in the most varied forms. It can, as with birds, extend over thousands of miles; some kinds of butterflies cross high mountain chains. Reindeer migrate over large stretches of the North. Eels, which breed in the Sargasso Sea, move eastwards and go up the rivers of the Eurasian continent. Salmon take the reverse path, from streams and rivers back into the ocean. Migratory locusts, which destroy everything in their path, and the hordes of migratory ants, swarm and creep in overwhelming numbers across vast land areas.

The migration of herring, the emergence of sturgeons, seals, sea-lions and penguins at definite times of the year, and their disappearance after shorter or longer periods, are all partial manifestations of this incessant coming and going.

Is there a single cause at the root of this roaming and migrating? It is an uncommonly complex phenomenon, which appears to depend on the most varied conditions. Each species has its own form of migration, and this is just as characteristic for it as the structure of its body or the arrangement of its teeth. Some migration is subject to seasonal rhythms; some follows the phases of the moon. Often the mating and birth periods are closely connected with the change of place. There are also nomadic animals which follow their source of food, and others that are suddenly seized by a migration mania and, like the Scandinavian lemmings, run straight to their deaths. When we try to find the essential features of migration, amid this multiplicity of phenomena, we find that the only way is to define the idea of migration as widely as possible. The more comprehensively we learn to look at the phenomenon, the more clearly its essential characteristics come to light.

A beehive in which regular activity has reigned for weeks on end, which has gathered nectar and pollen, cared for the larvae, taught the young bees their occupations and functions, is suddenly seized by a general unrest. All regularity is interrupted. Foraging has already been low for several days; the queen cells, in which future queens are almost ready to come out, are strictly guarded. Then, often when the sun breaks through after a short period of rain, in a moment the bees begin to swarm. The old queen and a large number of young bees leave the hive and go as a compact swarm in search of a new hive.

The Norwegian lemming, a kind of vole, can live for years in the plateaux and high moors of the northern mountains — solitary, hardly noticed, very shy and withdrawn. Then one summer, when breeding has been more plentiful than usual and a multitude of young lemmings populates the heathlands, the urge to migrate breaks over them. By the thousands they mob together, become quarrelsome and aggressive, run through woods and bush, cross rivers, plunge into deep gorges, suffocate one another, pressed body to body, and always they rush on towards the west until they reach the coast, and at last, driven on without pause, they perish in the ocean.

The penguins, having avoided the shores of Antarctica for months, suddenly emerge, as if touched with a magic wand; by the hundreds they come out of the ocean, and, crowded cheek by jowl, populate the solid land. Here they build their enclosures — pits or small depressions surrounded by stones. In these they lay their eggs and hatch their young. When the youngsters have learnt to swim, the penguins troop back into the sea and disappear, no-one knows where, for the rest of the year.

These examples could be supplemented with many others. In each case we see that, along with the occurrence of migration, another element appears. The individual creatures band together into greater or smaller groups. Birds, fish, insects — they all swarm and set off towards their goal in serried companies.

Many explanations for this behaviour have been offered. Each one of these theories contains a bit of truth, but none does justice to the phenomenon itself in all its aspects. Certainly hunger, sexual instinct, and expectation of death, play a role in it; but what brings about this banding together? What impels the individual to seek community with members of its species and to undertake these migrations, journeys and wedding flights only with them? Why do thousands of penguins, tens of thousands of seals, millions of herrings, eels, and sardines suddenly crowd together? Some kinds journey together, others settle down in numberless multitudes in certain places.

Can we grasp intuitively what occurs in these moments of animal life? Of course, one can try to put the responsibility for it on a glandular function, the sudden awakening of an instinct, and other things; but the glands change their functioning, the instincts awake, because something higher, stronger, permeates the whole species and transforms it.

What happens to a group of birds in the autumn when they take up the wanderer's staff, so to speak, and fly south? A sudden unrest comes over them; banding together occurs and the travelling begins. Birds of passage which are kept in cages experience the same unrest when their relatives at liberty are beginning to migrate. Lucanus writes (1929):

SEALS

> The frenzied captive flaps about tirelessly in its cage,
> and often damages its plumage almost beyond
> recognition . . . This proves with certainty that it is
> not outer causes which impel the migratory bird to
> its travels, but that it follows an all-powerful drive
> which masters it completely and cannot voluntarily
> be suppressed or changed. The bird of passage
> migrates because it must!

But why must birds migrate? Because all living creatures,
including human beings, are imbued with certain rhythms
of life. It is not justified to compare even approximately
the migratory drive of animals with the human being's
desire for travel and search for knowledge. This error has
repeatedly blocked the way to true insights. Animals and
birds migrate and return in the same way that human
beings sleep and wake.

Birds preparing for their flight south experience a
change of consciousness to which they must yield. It is
an experience of falling asleep, of evening, which comes
over them. Then they begin to dream of the South, and
each species has its communal dream; its members come
together in the experience of this dream and find their
way, like sleepwalkers, to the land of their dreams. A
change of behaviour comes about in all of them. Lucanus
relates (1929):

> On the Courland Spit I could often observe how
> migratory falcons and sparrow-hawks journeyed in
> the immediate vicinity of thrushes, starlings, finches,
> or other small birds, without showing the least
> desire for prey, and all the small birds paid no
> attention whatever to the otherwise dreaded
> predators, but continued their air journeys quite
> near them, not even changing their direction of
> flight in the least degree.

This can be explained only by the fact that all these birds,
predators and prey, have become dreamers. A light sleep
has come over them, and during their stay in the South

they will not wake from this sleep until the early morning of their return journey dawns. Then they begin to strive back towards their homeland, back to daytime work — nest-building, hatching, bringing up the young. When this work is done, the evening of departure, the dream of the South, begins to come over them once more.

Here is revealed the powerful background which underlies all animal migration. As we human beings sleep and wake in the rhythm of the daily revolution of the earth, so are birds and animals subject to a similar, but yearly, rhythm. Not the earth, but the interplay of earth, sun, and moon sets the rhythm of their sleeping and waking. Migrating and returning is an experience of falling asleep and awakening for the group souls of the individual species. The overwhelming power of this phenomenon is simply not to be explained on the basis of instincts, drives and modes of behaviour alone. A mighty soul-breath passes through the individual races: breathing out, it lifts them from their daytime work into a dreamland; breathing in, it leads them back to everyday life.

The life of the seals can be thoroughly understood only when we see these great breaths which flow across the earth. This large animal group, about which so many mysteries are woven, is governed by this rhythm in a special way, as we shall now show.

2 The annual cycle

The life of most seals is determined largely by an alternation between migration and rest. The swinging of this life-pendulum is emphasized by the fact that one period of it takes place mostly in the element of water, and the other entirely on dry land. The length of the periods varies with the species and their environments. Some spend half the time on land, others only a few weeks.

In all species of seals the young are born only on land,

never in the water. Pairing as well takes place on land, soon after the birth of offspring; and the pups, helpless and utterly dependent on maternal care, come to know the sea only after some time, under their mothers' guidance and leadership. In small pools on the shore they receive proper swimming instruction, until they have mastered the element of water. Then it is the wide spaces of the ocean for them, and when they return to dry land, they are grown up.

The young seals grow and develop in swift steps. The milk teeth, in those species which have them, are lost before, or soon after, birth. The weight increase in seal pups is about one and a half kilograms (3 lb) a day. Thus the young grow amazingly fast, and are weaned just a month after birth.

Only one pup is born at a time, and if the mother, forgetting herself, swims out for a day or two and does not look after her child, or perhaps does not return, it will starve. The young begin to whine pitifully, and real tears run out of their great dark eyes.

After the suckling period, the pups stay for one more month, unwatched, on shore. The mothers have lost interest in them and live in the harems of their husbands. The young continue to grow, although taking hardly any nourishment; their coat changes colour, and when the storms of the oncoming winter begin and cold days set in, all the seals, young and old, move out into the ocean. Where they go is not known, but they undertake long journeys. Seals ringed in Norway have been found the following year in southern Sweden, Scotland, and Iceland. The majority go back to their old breeding grounds, and their return proceeds according to strict rules.

The ursine seals living in the northern Pacific, from Alaska to Kamchatka, begin to appear at their breeding grounds towards the end of May. First come the older, powerful males, soon followed by the younger seals.

THE ANNUAL CYCLE

Throughout the month of June there is a continual struggle for suitable nesting sites. Each of the older bulls encircles his domain — a few square metres in size — with a few stones and clods of earth, but above all with his anger and jealousy. Thousands of these precincts lie next to each other; and the young males, who cannot yet claim a nesting place, stay more or less respectfully in the surrounding area.

Then, around midsummer, and on into the first days of July, thousands of females climb out of the sea and allow the bulls to lead them into their domains. The stronger the male the greater the number of his wives. Not many days after this the children are born, are suckled and raised, and at the same time new matings take place.

In the Antarctic, where the southern seals live, the same process occurs, only it begins in November and lasts until March of the next year.

During all this time the seals take in no food. Their life is leisure and idleness now, not hunting and preying. It is also strife among the males; it is love-play and comfort. The little pups grow and get up to their childish mischief. All observers, such as Lockley (1954), who have lived at such a breeding ground for many weeks, have always been captivated by the magic world of this existence.

What goes on at all these places where seals settle down on land is a picture of their involvement in the course of the sun. When the sun is climbing towards its yearly culmination, the seals climb out of the sea on to land. They leave the sea not because the climate is getting warmer and living conditions are better on land. The sun carries them out of the depths of the water into the heights of the air. It is a summer lulling-to-sleep that takes place. The seals are permeated by dream-pictures, and must give themselves to them.

This is the reverse of what happens with migratory

15

birds. For them, breeding and hatching are day-work. The seals have moved it into their realm of summer sleep and dreams. Such differences are of great importance for the study of biology and the history of the earth, and deserve to be investigated much more deeply than they have been so far. When autumn comes and the sun loses its strength and sinks downwards, the seals wake up again. Autumn is their morning. Then they go back into the water and become predators and hunters; now they begin their day-work.

This periodicity within the year has yet another aspect. Within the great circle of mammals, the seals (Pinnipedia) form their own order. Some researchers count them among the predators; certain features are indicative of dogs. Their character and way of life make it difficult to include them in any other order. They have some traits which relate them to the carnivores, others relating them to elephants. In the water they are predators, dreaded hunters; no fish is safe from them. They are also capable of amazing swimming feats; they are swift, bold, and eager to attack. In the sea they do not seem to live in herds, but remain solitary, only loosely connected with other members of their species. Their movements are characterised by exceptional skill and suppleness.

On land, however, seals are clumsy; since the upper arms and thighs have remained, in a very shortened form, within the skin and the rest of the limbs have been transformed into finlike appendages, locomotion is greatly hindered. They crawl, propping and dragging themselves along the ground. They also give up their predatory ways. They draw together in small herds reminiscent of hoofed animals. One bull rules the herd, which consists of a varying number of females and their young. Elephants have similar social tendencies.

Thus the seals swing back and forth not only between water and land, but also, in their character, between predator and hoofed animal. During their waking period they resemble the former; during their dreaming period, the latter.

In addition, seals have certain almost human traits, or at least seemingly anthropoid ones. A mother gives birth to only a single pup or, rarely, she may have twins. The young pup can whine and cry tears, and even has milk teeth. The human expression of the seal's face comes about because the eyes are large and round, and because the head has an almost spherical top. In some species, especially the sea-dogs, the forehead projects over the eyes, and since the snout is not pushed forward too far, the resemblance to a human face arises.

I was standing once at dusk on the beach at Tintagel, quite near to Merlin's cave, and the sea was singing its dark song, when a sea-dog suddenly emerged out of the water. He looked at me with questioning curiosity, and our eyes met. It was a look such as I have scarcely ever exchanged in such immediacy with an animal: a look without fear, without shyness, with full understanding of the situation. It was then that I began to awaken to the riddle of these strange creatures.

3 Habitat and origin

In the history of the earth, no ancestors point towards the seals. The skeletons and skeletal impressions of them described by palaeontology show the same structures found in the species living in our time: the stumpy limbs, the regressive tail, and the characteristic formation of the teeth. The findings have been made almost exclusively in those geological layers corresponding to the two initial periods of the Tertiary — the Miocene and the Pliocene.

The facts indicate clearly that the order of seals arose comparatively late, and probably quite suddenly. Wherever their remains have been found, they show the characteristic features, with no earlier or intermediate stages. Suddenly, in full and perfected form, they are there.

At first one can hardly doubt that the seals were origi-
nally land animals. They are still lung-breathing, and their
newborn are so organized that they cannot live in the sea
during the beginning of their life. For the moment we
must suppose that all seals went from land into the water,
and, as in dreaming remembrance, return each year to
the home of their origin, guided by the sun.

Where are the shores to which they find their way, and
where do the seals have their chief breeding grounds?
The latest surveys show unequivocally that the original
centres around which they lived were the two polar areas.
The Arctic as well as the Antarctic are still their habitat
today (Scheffer 1958).

Certain species, such as the sea leopards, certain kinds
of sea-lions and elephant seals, inhabit the Antarctic.
Others emerge to mate and raise their young on many
islands and peninsulas extending round the North Pole:
Greenland and Iceland, the eastern and western shores
of Northern Canada, and the islands stretching between
America and Asia and reaching from Alaska to Kamchatka and Sakhalin. Since the seals pass their summer
sleep and dream without taking in food, the barren,
stony, often ice and snow-bound world of the polar shores
is a possible habitat for them.

Some seals, however, especially among the sea-dogs,
find their way along the coasts towards the south. In
Europe they are regularly seen in Ireland, Wales and
Cornwall. They can appear in Portugal; and a certain
group, the monk-seal, even inhabits the shores of the
Mediterranean. The further south they go, the less clear
the yearly periodicity of their existence becomes. They
play back and forth between water and land and lose
their original life-rhythm.

They also inhabit inland seas, such as Lake Baikal
and the Caspian Sea, and this could be a key to their
geographical distribution. Perhaps the waves of the ice-
age floods, pushing southwards, first brought them there,

and left them when the floods retreated. The palaeontological findings also support this supposition: seal skeletons have been found in South Russia, in Hungary, in Italy, and even in Egypt.

It is from the North, around the Arctic, that the different seal families seem to come. There, near the Pole, was their original home, and many still return there today. The southward-moving glaciers of the ice-ages brought the seals with them. The wider the ice-belt became, the further southwards it pushed the original polar animals. From the Antarctic as well, individual branches of the seal family push northwards along the coasts of South America, reaching as far as Patagonia; and the sea-lions extend beyond the equator. Australia and New Zealand are likewise habitats of the seals.

Can we form a coherent picture of the seals out of these few palaeontological and geographical findings, and with it decipher their background in the history of the earth? From the north polar regions they have been driven step by step into the temperate zones, on the successive waves of the ice-ages, but the polar regions have remained their home. Now the nearer we come to the poles, the more the sun's yearly course dominates the daily rhythm, so natural for other parts of the earth. Earth day and earth night are transformed into polar day and polar night. For months on end the sun does not appear over the horizon, until it rises in the spring, not to set again for many weeks. Here we meet the same periodicity that is inscribed into the life-rhythm of the seals. During the time of the polar night, the sinking sun takes its seal-children with it, and they plunge into the waters of the great oceans. When the sun rises for the polar day, all over the earth the seals follow it and clamber on to the land. The whole order of seals is permeated by this polar sun-rhythm. And it is this fact that first enables us to understand the geographical distribution and life-style of these animals.

The prehistory of seals — which we have been able to uncover from their geographical distribution and mode of behaviour — and their rhythm of life, which follows the polar course of the sun, lead us back in the history of the earth to those regions where, at the beginnings of terrestrial and human evolution, we can look for the Hyperboreans. At that time, everything which was later to unfold as the human race and the kingdoms of nature still lived in a germinal state. Rudolf Steiner described it once in the following way (1971, 54f [1908 Sep 7]):

> It was a collective world-womb in which the light-plant man lived at that time, feeling himself one with the light-mantle of the earth. In this refined vaporous plant-form, man hung as though on the umbilical cord of the earth-mother and he was cherished and nourished by the whole mother earth. As in a cruder sense the child of today is cherished and nourished in the maternal body, so the human germ was cherished and nourished at that time.

During this period the sun separated from the earth. 'As a result of this departure of the sun, the mist cooled to water.' In this way the 'water-sphere' arose, and the human being was so fashioned that he 'protruded into the mist-sheath, so that he was half a water, half a vapor-being'. There the light reached him from outside, from the surrounding sun.

Now the mystery of the origin of the seals begins to be deciphered. In that region of the earth which is still the home of many seals today, there once lay the cradle of human kind. There the human bodies lived, light flowing all around them, air shining through them, 'on the umbilical cord of the earth-mother'. They condensed and solidified more and more as time passed. Rudolf Steiner, in the lecture quoted above (1971, 56), indicates that at the time when the sun left the earth, man's body had reached that stage which 'we see preserved today in a degenerated form in fishes. The fishes that we see in the water today are relics of those men . . .'

But seals are not fish, and yet they are formed and structured for life in the water. If we ask what separates seal and fish from one another, the answer is not hard to find. The seals are closer to man; they are mammals; they form social ties, at least while they are living on land; and they give birth to a single offspring and raise it, if only for a few weeks.

Fish, by contrast, entrust their eggs, often in unending numbers, to the element of water; and even if a few species do build nests and tend to their young for a short time, an infinite distance separates them from the mammals, and especially from the order of seals, in structure, being and behaviour.

The fish is a water-creature, but the seal-organism is only adapted to life in the water. The limbs are transformed into swimming appendages; the skin is padded underneath with a thick layer of fat; this provides a necessary warmth-shield, and so the round, spindle-shaped body is well suited for swimming. The ear and nose openings can be completely closed in the water. Thus all these characteristics are those of sea-dwellers.

But where do we place the origin of the seals? Were they really once land-dwelling mammals that later went into the water? If this were so, we ought to find at least some indications of earlier stages of these sea-dwellers — but in fact the seals appear fully formed in the two last periods of the Tertiary — the Miocene and the Pliocene. According to Wachsmuth's investigations (1950), these geological epochs correspond to the beginnings of the Atlantis era; this means that when the primal forms of the mammals were first beginning to develop, the seals appear already fully formed. Is there not here a contradiction which calls for an explanation?

Might the seals be the ancestors of all the mammals which arose at that time? Not ancestors in the sense of a theory of evolution in which one animal is said to arise from another by apparent forces of heredity and adaptation, but forerunners in the sense that they have kept their primitive physical form, their rudimentary limbs, and their round bodies, without specializing them? Probably the seals were never really land animals, since it was not until the middle of the Atlantean era that the earth became solid enough for animals and humans to stand and take firm foothold on it.

If we follow up these considerations, we can approach the seal's body as a new object-lesson. Is it not reminiscent of an embryonic form? A human embryo at the end of the second month, though not much longer than 25 mm (one inch), has a form and structure very like that of a seal. In the embryo the limbs are still no more than insignificant stumps; the eyes are round, their lids held wide apart. The mouth has no lips — it is like a slit. And the embryo floats in the water of the amniotic-sac enveloping it.

Are we meeting here the early history of the earth? The seals did not become fish, because they stayed within the human family even into the beginning of Atlantean times. They had undifferentiated, embryo-like bodies that moved half floating, half swimming in the still uncondensed water-earth. At the beginning of Atlantis, when memory and language were forming (Steiner 1959 [1908]) and man's ancestors — among them the seals — were taking the first steps towards 'I'-development, the decline of the seals began. They entered too quickly into densification and hardened their embryonic human form. This is why even today they lose their milk teeth at the time of birth and are suckled for only a few weeks. At this time they grow so fast that they very soon become independent. Their hurried childhood is a clear indication of the precipitous process by which they became animals.

The seals bear witness that mankind's first origins lay in those Hyperborean regions which surround the North

Pole in a broad belt in the early days of the earth. Here were the ancestors of man, and also the ancestors of the seals; the two were identical. At the beginning of Atlantis, when the development of personality-consciousness began to emerge, part of the gradually developing human race while still in an embryonic form, fell prematurely into solidification. They became the order of the seals. They are the proto-mammals, which became capable of reproduction as embryonic forms.*

However, they have kept not only their embryonic form but also the inner connection to the sun which once permeated the Hyperborean regions. In the rhythm of polar night and polar day, they still follow the sun's course. They were never actually land animals — quite the contrary. Out of the waters of early Atlantis, into which they plunged all too soon, they attempted to take foot on the earth, which was gradually becoming denser. They did not quite succeed. Every year they make this attempt afresh, and in a touching gesture entrust their young to the dry land; but it is only a dream, and passes away as quickly as it came. When the storms of autumn come on, they have to go back into the sea, for the setting polar sun is calling them.

That is the earthly destiny of all the seals: as human embryos they densified too soon, and had to submerge themselves in the waters of the great oceans. They reached the Antarctic, where they found conditions like those of their former home. Again and again they try to attain the land, and always the water overcomes them. They represent a world-wide monument to an early stage of human evolution. When we look into their eyes, we see ourselves as we once were, and we sense dimly how we have evolved and what they, the seals, still are.

They are so near to us because they did not become

---

* They are typical representatives of the biological phenomenon called neoteny.

specialized like the other mammals. They are neither normal carnivores nor ungulates. They are not forms reminding us of Lemurian times, like the marsupials and the monotremes, nor those forms given to destructiveness which we know as the rodents.

They are related to the whales and dolphins, but these have another origin again. The seals later went through the Atlantean catastrophe and thus came into all those regions of the earth which they still populate today.

4 Mythology

The Eskimos once lived in close connection with seals and whales. Formerly, when a sea-dog or a walrus was taken by the hunt, the successful hunter stayed in his hut for three days. During this time he was not allowed to take food or drink, nor to touch his wife. All work in his house was left aside; the bedding was not straightened and the blubber-oil not wiped off from the lamps.

After three days the soul of the slain seal was free and went back into its mother's womb. Then daily life and hunting could begin again. The souls of the seals, walruses, and whales go home to Sedna, the great goddess (Frazer, 1911, 3:210):

> [Dr Franz Boas] tells us, the mother of the sea-mammals, may be considered to be the chief deity of the central Esquimaux. She is supposed to bear supreme sway over the destinies of mankind . . .
> Her home is in the lower world; where she dwells in a house built of stones and whale-ribs. 'The souls of seals, ground seals, and whales are believed to proceed from her home. After one of these animals has been killed, its soul stays with the body for three days. Then it goes back to Sedna's abode, to be sent forth again by her.'

An extraordinary number of rites and taboos among the Eskimos are connected with the seals. The souls of these animals are 'endowed with much greater gifts than those of men'. What they cannot stand is the vapour that rises from human blood, and the shadow and dark colour of death. Menstruating women are also intolerable to them.

The Eskimos sense dimly that blood and death contain those 'I'-forces and personality motifs from which the seals once withdrew. They still belong to the goddess of the underworld and the earth's depths; they belong to the realm of the mothers, where man's destiny began. Rudolf Steiner said (1981 [1917 Nov 2]) that the 'mothers' are to be found in the bygone stages of earth's development. The souls of the seals reach back to those regions of the past; there they have their common origin with human beings, their brothers.

The latter, however, have denied this brotherhood in recent centuries. In the north and the south of the earth, they began a truly merciless hunt against their own ancestors. Millions of sea-dogs, walruses, sea-lions, leopard seals, and fur seals have been annihilated. With clubs, axes, guns, and knives whole tribes have been exterminated and species brought to extinction. This was not done by the Eskimos, who lived in close connection with the seals. It was done out of greed for money and plunder by Europeans, Japanese, and Americans. Now the seals are becoming even scarcer, and the house of the goddess Sedna must be crowded with their souls. This mother-goddess of the earth's depths also keeps watch over the fate of human beings; but what can become of a mankind that destroys the image of its infancy? Is it not denying its divine origin?

Only a very few people still know the true story of the origin of the seals. Even the Lapp Aslak, son of Siri Matti, who told of the seal's origin on May 24, 1944, 'as the fathers have handed down', retains only an intuitive sense of the truth. He spoke of the exodus of the Jews out of Egypt, of their crossing the Red Sea, and of the Egyptians pursuing them: 'Then Moses raised up his staff again, and Pharaoh and all his men, dogs, carts and horses were swallowed by the waters. Pharaoh himself and all who belonged to his kind turned into seals; they became big seals, while all his soldiers became little seals.'*

Here again we see, though in a historically distorted form, an archetypal picture of the seal's origin. One part of humanity, that does not take part in the progress of evolution but wants to prevent it, is swallowed by the waters. The other part goes with dry feet through the sea, and reaches land on the other side.

And at the end of his story Aslak added this comment: 'If you pay attention when you take the skin off a seal, it looks almost like a man. Especially when you lay a seal on its belly.' So Aslak divined the deep kinship of seal and man.

* For the text of this story, I am indebted to Professor Kohl-Larsen who heard it with me and took it down. I would also like to thank him warmly at this point for his valuable help.

The Life of Penguins

1 Habitat around Antarctica

In his well-known book, *The Island of Penguins*, Cherry Kearton writes (1930, x-xi):

> Indeed, I doubt whether, in more than forty years of nature study throughout the world, I have ever found a creature so interesting and withal so amusing. Thanks to the comical expressions for which he is famous, you cannot help laughing at him. But the Island of Penguins has taught me that he is not only to be laughed at. He may not always seem especially intelligent — though he does, presumably by instinct, many exceedingly wise and careful things — but he is virtuous and faithful; and as a model in married life he is supreme.

Whoever has seen penguins will confirm this description. These birds are strange folk. They cannot fly, but waddle in an upright position on land, or slide forwards on their bellies. In their thousands they emerge suddenly from the sea, to settle at their breeding-places. Then they are like the sand on the seashore. A few weeks after pairing, the female lays one egg. The partners share the brooding, and with touching care they together tend to the upbringing of their (usually single) offspring. All this takes place *en masse*, cheek by jowl and nest to nest.

After the young have become independent to some extent, the penguins all go back into the sea.

Every year this rhythm is repeated, the only difference being that the various species of penguins have individual rhythms. Most of them breed during the summer. The emperor penguins, however, come ashore in autumn and pass their hatching and rearing time there in the winter. The gentoo penguins even nest twice a year, in autumn as well as in the springtime. To be sure, they live nearer the temperate zone than do most of their relatives.

The penguins are creatures of the Antarctic. Their habitat reaches from the Antarctic continent to the islands and island groups of the surrounding ocean. This entire region is used by the penguins as breeding grounds. It extends from New Zealand across Tasmania to the Kerguelen and Crozet Islands, and South Africa, all the way to South Georgia, South Orkney and South Shetlands. Cold ocean currents even brought them to the Galapagos Islands on the Equator. In the north polar region penguins are unknown.

It is a noteworthy phenomenon that we encounter here for very few kinds of birds or animals have so clearly limited a dwelling zone. How is this to be understood? Is not the North Pole similar to the South Pole? Both represent regions separated from the rest of the earth, regions where the daily rhythm has become a yearly rhythm because the sun rises and sets only once in the course of twelve months. The region of eternal ice covers both polar zones; but within this cover the two realms are completely different (Banse 1932).

> The North Polar region is a great caved-in basin, a
> trough out of which remnants of islands project,
> surrounded by the coastal faces of the continents.
> By contrast, the South Polar region is a continent,
> an extended upland block surrounded by sea.

This characterizes the basic contrast between the two polar regions.

The following description brings this out even more clearly (Hermann, 1959):

> The North Pole is situated in a deep ocean the size
> of the continent of Europe, and over 4 200 metres
> [14 000 feet] deep at the Pole itself. The South Pole,
> by contrast, is the midpoint (at least approximately)

of a great continent half again the size of Europe.
It lies on a plateau, about 2 900 metres [10 000 feet]
above sea-level. Thus, while the enormous land
masses of Asia, Europe, and America form an
almost closed ring around the deep, wide ocean basin
at the North Pole, the continent of the South Pole
— the earth's sixth continent — lies totally isolated
in a great ocean 5 000 metres [16 000 feet] deep.
The Atlantic, the Pacific, and the Indian Ocean flow
together into an immeasurable water-mass.

If we try to bring our picture of the two poles into
sharper focus, and picture to ourselves that the Arctic
Ocean goes down 4 000 metres (13 000 feet) and the
Antarctic continent is almost 3 000 metres (10 000 feet)
high, so that there is a difference of 7 000 metres (23 000
feet) in height — and if we consider further that in the
North we have a sea surrounded with shores, but in the
South a giant island surrounded by the sea, then the
contrast becomes still more evident in its archetypal
clarity. The North Pole is an ocean hemmed in by the
shores of the great continents; the South Pole an island
swept by mighty oceans.

Sea and island are the two primal forms which mould
the landscape of the earth in almost endless variety. The
archetypal island is the South Pole. The archetypal sea is
the Arctic; and from these two realms comes the forma-
tive power flowing into all other regions of the earth. We
could almost say that all islands, wherever they may lie,
are children of the Antarctic; and the oceans, however
small or large, are creations of the North Polar basin.

An island — every island — is a piece of earth which
has condensed, crystallized out of the surrounding water.
The forces active in the fluid element concentrate themselves at a midpoint and give rise to the island. An ocean,
by contrast, is a dissolving process which forms in the
centre of the realm of hard earth. From its midpoint
the dissolving, liquefying forces flow to the surrounding

shores, carrying away cliffs and mountains in the course of thousands of years.

The island is a process of solidification into earth; the sea is a dissolving, a passing away of earth. Condensation and dissolution are the forces active in these two forms. The North Pole is old; there the earth is dissolving. From there the ice ages breathe rhythmically into the course of evolution, covering parts of the northern continents with ice for hundreds of years and then withdrawing to the mother of all seas. From the South Pole, on the other hand, the solidifying island-forces flow into the earth. They hold the continents together and give the earth-realm its hardening properties.

Dissolution flows out of the North, but it is held in balance by the great continental land masses, so that the earth does not become completely fluid. Solidification works from the South; the oceanic water masses oppose this gigantic power, so that the earth does not harden completely.

These are the contrasts between the two polar regions. The wave-like beauty of the seas, which imbues any landscape with a dreamy, intuitive element, since the heavens are reflected in their waters and see themselves there — this comes from the North. The hardening rigour inherent in all islands, which put a stop to the waters and offer to the sky not a mirror but a fist — this comes from the South. Here the earth can stand on its own, and resists the sky.

The penguins are creatures of these forces of self-will. They gather together in places where earth-condensation and island-formation have their sphere of action.

2 Fish or bird?

Why do we have the feeling, whenever we encounter the penguins, of being a little above them, and we cannot help expressing this in a slight smile? And when we think of these small creatures that carry themselves upright, why do we feel a sort of tragi-comical sympathy for them?

Is it his caricature of a bird that makes us laugh at the penguin? He is a bird and also not a bird; he cannot fly, and his two wings are atrophied stumps that he moves up and down like deformed arms covered with scale-like feathers. When a penguin stretches out his arms, it seems a pitiful gesture; we can see that these stunted limbs could never raise his round body into the air. But the fact that he cannot fly makes this bird not a ridiculous but a tragic figure.

The comical element has another root; does it not come from the penguin seeming to imitate a human being? Instead of flying, he sets himself upright when he walks, begins to chatter and screech, and takes himself so seriously — as if he were really somebody. This is how it seems to us, and so we smile. It is as if a fish, whose fins had turned into feet, were to climb on to the land and begin to strut about.

The penguin is actually a bird metamorphosed into a fish. His realm is the water, that is where he feels completely at home. In Brehms (1911) we read:

> Generally they swim for a distance of about 30 metres [100 feet] under water, then they jump, like little dolphins, up to 30 cm [12 inches] above the surface — presumably to breathe — and quickly disappear into the water again. In this locomotion they make use only of their wings; they fly in the water, as it were . . . And they move through the water with extraordinary speed – so fast, according to Chun, that they can overtake a steamship with playful ease.

In Gerlach (1964) we read:

> With their wings they are no longer able to fly, but they make a flying motion with them under water. Their fin-wings turn in a rapid, wide swing, up to two hundred strokes a minute. The penguins speed along in their underwater flight, putting ten metres behind them in a second [22 miles per hour].

Thus they can easily swim a kilometre in two minutes, and thirty in an hour. Is it then so strange that no one can fathom where they go when they leave the islands with their grown offspring and disappear into the sea? Maybe all southern seas up to the Equator are their habitat.

When they come on to the land to lay and hatch their eggs — that is when we first begin to find them comical. As if in remembrance of their past, they take on the life of birds; the young males and females find one another, build nests, and a respectable family life begins. The swift hunter has turned into a good citizen. His upright carriage, and the striking design and colouring of his coat of feathers — with a white shirt-front covering his whole abdomen, and a black back like coat-tails — bring out this respectability even more closely. They stand together in thousands, chattering, gossiping, pushing one another, taking each other's stones for nest-building, on occasion even stealing a wife and her well-guarded egg, but in spite of all they are good wives and husbands, and faithful parents.

These characteristics, which have been carefully observed and thoroughly described, make the penguin a comical figure while on land. He must be a bird, and yet he cannot be one; he lacks wings, and therefore is bound to the earth. To overcome this lack, he tries to be like a human being, but this bold attempt fails miserably. So the penguin lives an unsuccessful existence, condemned to leave behind his home in the sea for half the year, to climb on to the land and live as an in-between form, to recall and repeat his former life as a bird, while at the same time he stands upright like a man, without being able to be one. Who is not reminded of curses and magic spells enchanting men into the bodies of animals, or condemning beings to spend part of their existence in places which will be torture for them? We think of how Demeter's daughter is sent down to the kingdom of the underworld, and allowed to come to the light for only a few months. A similar secret lies hidden in the life of the penguins, covered over with a mask of incompleteness and comicality. Has Circe, the powerful sorceress, daughter of Helios, had a hand in this?

3 Non-flying birds

On the shores and islands of the Arctic there are no penguins. Yet up to the beginning of the last century birds of a special kind lived there, comparable to the penguins: the great auks. Although they belong to a quite different branch of the race of birds, they were subject to a similar restructuring. In the great auk, too, the wings became stunted limbs and the power of flight was lost. In size he was like the larger species of penguins, measuring about 90 cm (3 feet). Like the penguin, he had a white breast and a black back. His nearest relatives are the razor-bill and the guillemot of the Scandinavian cliffs.

In earlier times the great auk inhabited not only the islands of the northern seas; prehistoric remains have been found also on the coasts of Denmark and Ireland, and even in southern parts of North America.* The last living specimens were sighted in and around Greenland as late as about 1820. Since then these birds, which may have been as numerous as penguins are today, have

* The penguin's name also has its origin in the North. The seamen called the great auk, which they knew, Pen-Gwyn, white-head. This comes from two Celtic words (*pen*: head; and *gwyn*: white), which were later transferred to the penguin, so similar to the great auk. But only in English and German; the French say *pingouin* for the auk and *manchot* for the penguin.

disappeared from the earth. In historical times they could be met with most often in Newfoundland, Greenland and Iceland.

> All observers mention that they [the great auks] used to swim with heads raised high, but with necks withdrawn, and they always dived when startled. They would sit up straight on cliffs, more upright than the guillemots and razor-billed auks. They walked or ran along with short little steps, upright like a man; and when in danger they dived four or five metres [15 feet] down into the sea. (Brehm 1911).

The great auk brooded in the summer and laid a single egg.

Thus in the Arctic forms of life similar to those we still find in the penguins had come into being. Both lost the status of birds in giving up the power of flight and in return acquired the capacity to swim. The great auk and the penguin, though probably not related genealogically, were subject to the same destiny. Have any other birds had a similar fate? We know of a number of such birds, some still living, others extinct. First of all comes the family of the ostriches. Their wings are atrophied and have such soft feathers that they are useless for flying. The neck and legs, however, are strongly developed, and a fully grown ostrich often reaches a height of over two metres (7 feet). The Australian cassowary, the South American nandu, and the moa of New Zealand (now extinct for centuries) have a similar build. The moa reached a height of three and a half to four metres (12 feet) and had powerful thighs and neck. And we still find, very isolated and rare, the flightless kiwi, the New Zealand apteryx.

All these birds have lost the power of flight. In return they have developed (except for the kiwi) powerful legs and elongated necks. It is as though in these parts of their bodies they had made good their loss of wings. We think immediately of Goethe's poem *The Metamorphosis of Animals*:

> Yet within a spirit seems to struggle mightily,
> How it can break the circle and foist its wanton will
>   upon the forms;
> But whatever it may try, it tries in vain;
> For though it penetrates to this limb or to that,
> And furnishes them grandly, still other parts soon
>   wither in return,
> The burden of imbalance destroying
> All beauty of form and all pure movement.

Ostriches and cassowaries are said to move quite gracefully while still young. The older and larger they become, the more the 'burden of imbalance' of neck and legs comes to the fore, and the grosser and more awkward are their movements. The wings and the power to fly were consumed by the legs and the running. In order to keep a balance with the formation of powerful lower limbs, the neck was pushed up away from the body, producing the present forms.

These flightless birds (again with the exception of the kiwi) live on the wide-open steppe. Sand, sun, short grass and dryness are their world. The great Madagascar ostriches (Aepyornithes) were, in Portmann's opinion (1957) gradually destroyed because:

> The progressive clearing of the light, savanna-like
> woods of many parts of Madagascar forced the animal
> life of these woods more and more into the
> swampier, less accessible areas of virgin forest . . .
> In these swampy wooded regions, the giant ostrich
> fell prey to crocodiles.

Moreover, the habitat of these birds was the steppe, not swampy woods; for this reason also they died off.

In all these birds the forces of the dry earth predominated. They dried out their bodies, refined their coat of feathers, and the flier became a runner. (In the kiwi, the power of the wings went into the elongated, curved bill.) It is characteristic that these birds live mainly in the southern half of the earth.

Are they not real opposites to the penguins? Both groups had their wings cropped by fate. In the penguins, however, the neck and legs were not extended, but drawn in. In every penguin the head sits directly on the breast; the feet stick out like short, absurd stumps from under the belly. Here the air has not dried out the body — quite the contrary: damp and darkness have filled out the body so that the legs and neck disappeared into it. This form reminds us of the whale, the seal and the dolphin. The limbs become little finlike appendages because the bodies, rounded with fat, swell up like balloons.

In the far North as well as in the far South, where cold, darkness and water become overwhelming forces, the great auk and penguin arise as counterparts to the ostrich and cassowary. Is it still possible to recognize the hidden riddle in the existence of these creatures?

4 The annual cycle

In recent decades the behaviour of large penguin colonies has been thoroughly studied. It has been found that the rhythm of coming and going is different for the separate species. The gentoo penguins studied by Kearton, which live on Dassen Island, north of Cape Town, come back on land twice a year, in March and in September; both times eggs are laid and hatched, and the young crawl out. These penguins also tend to lay two eggs while the other species usually produce a single egg.

The emperor penguins, studied by a French group of researchers (Marret 1956, and Rivolier 1956), choose the Antarctic winter, the bleakest season there is, for brooding and rearing their young. Here it is no longer very convincing to speak of an instinct serving the preservation of the species. The young males and females begin to appear on the high ice plateaus of the Antarctic in April and May. The time of the deep polar night, the period of the worst hurricanes and the iciest cold, they spend without taking any nourishment, tending with touching devotion their new-born young.

As far as we know, most of the other species brood during the Antarctic spring and summer. Thus no uniform rhythm of life can be shown for the penguin family. The different species have their individual periods of migration.

Nevertheless, we cannot doubt that the appearance of the penguins at their nesting grounds is comparable to the return of all other migratory birds. For the penguins, brooding is the time of work and waking. They must suffer through love, birth, and struggle in these months; not until they return to the watery dreamland of the sea will their joy and play begin. What 'the South' is for the birds of our climes, the sea is for the penguins. They are not birds that just happened to fall into water: they have chosen the water as their paradise. They yearn for the water as other birds long to reach their far-away dreamland.

On land, however, they try to behave like all other birds although they cannot fly. They show birdlike gestures and courting customs. They build nests of the greatest variety, are monogamous for years together, and are especially attentive to their brooding. These avian behaviour forms are exaggerated in the penguins; often they are even caricatured and bizarrely distorted. Since they can walk upright, we see kissing scenes in the courting and mating season when the couple will rub beaks and even snuggle their heads together. The young male often spreads out his wing-stumps and tries to embrace his bride; this to the accompaniment of all sorts of noises, screams and barking sounds.

Nest-building is carried out communally by both partners. First one partner works, and when he is tired the other comes, until after some days the enclosure is ready (usually a depression in the ground, like a small cave). Their work done, man and wife climb down to the shore together to bathe and take their evening meal. Then they will meet a few acquaintances for a little chat, stroll along the main street, returning finally to the newly-built house.

The egg, laid after three to four weeks, is greeted with apparent amazement and joy, and once again it is both parents who tend the brooding, alternating with one another. This is a time of danger and threat. Rapacious gulls and ibises are hovering all around for a chance to steal the precious eggs and make a meal of them. Not more than half the chicks crawl out of the shell, and many fall prey to enemies and the inhospitable conditions.

For the young of the emperor penguins there is no nest. The egg is kept and hatched in an abdominal fold, and the baby penguin squats for weeks on his father's feet, enveloped, protected, and warmed by his abdomen. The mother is far away, somewhere out in the sea, eating to gather new forces. The fathers stand by the hundreds and thousands in the icy polar night, pressed close together to hold off the murderous, annihilating storms. They form whole clusters of penguins, giving each other the last measure of warmth they retain. Beneath this bird-cluster crouch the almost featherless baby penguins, waiting for the rays of the sun to return after weeks of absence. The life of the penguins is not all play. When they are on land, they carry their bird's destiny with them as a painful, oppressive memory; misery and need are their lot.

They must once have thrown off their bird-existence to acquire a different, perhaps better, life. So they dive into the ocean, but once or even twice a year they have to give up their enchantment and remember painfully their bird-existence. Kearton (1930, 83) describes how the young penguins at a few weeks of age are still quite shy of the water, and only the greatest effort and patience by their parents can induce them to make the first attempts at diving and swimming. Kearton adds something more. He says:

> Sometimes, curiously enough, they seem to imagine that their flippers are wings and that with a little practice they could fly . . . At any rate, I have often seen young birds deliberately flapping their wings as if they were quite certain that that was the way to do it . . . This attempt is so frequent that it cannot, I think, be only the easing of muscles. Perhaps it is all a legacy of former ages . . . when the penguins really did fly.

Very probably they could, and if so a series of events — or one event — must have brought about their loss of flight at some time. After the penguin was no longer able to fly, the wings shrivelled and became fins, which enabled him to live in the water. The Antarctic forces of island-formation and darkness, the forces of the great watery wastes, swelled up his body, which absorbed his legs and arms into itself. Thus out of a bird arose a fish; but a fish that has to be a bird every year, although it is hard and wearisome. The race would not live on if it did not make the sacrifice of going on land each year.

5 The two climaxes of a penguin's existence

During this period on land, the penguin becomes a caricature of a human being. He even succumbs to a regularly recurring illness: moulting. Moulting is of course a characteristic of the entire family of birds, but on most water birds it has the effect of making them quite unsure in flying for several weeks. Swans, ducks and geese cast off all their feathers at the same time. They hide in a thicket on the banks or in a marsh until their body-covering grows back and they can fly again.

Most birds moult in a less drastic way. The old feathers are lost little by little and are gradually replaced by the new. During the process the birds may look wretched, but they can fly and feed.

The penguin, however, is really ill with moulting. For several weeks he is unable to catch any food for, while some other birds lose their power of flight during a moult, he loses the power to swim. Kearton reports (1930, 89 & 93) that the penguins he observed moult regularly in December. They sense the oncoming of this illness for during the preceding days they eat much more than usual in order to have a little supply. ' . . . these penguins are like turkeys before Christmas . . . They just go on getting fatter and fatter — and then one day the first definite sign of moulting appears. From that moment all is misery for at least six weeks . . .' The strength for diving and swimming is lost. The search for food ceases; the bird leaves its nesting-place and lives homeless somewhere in the open. The feathers fall out in patches all over the body. 'You will see thousands of moulting penguins closely gathered on to one of these open spaces, each apparently more depressed than his neighbour.' Soon the whole island is covered a foot deep with feathers, these starving pictures of misery standing among them.

By the end of the moulting the penguins are so emaciated that they are too light to dive under the water. So now they begin to swallow small stones from the beach in order to reach the necessary weight. 'You can see them wandering on the seashore examining pebbles, rejecting some (as being too large, perhaps, or because their sides are not sufficiently smooth for easy swallowing), and gobbling up others till they think that the 'ballast' they have taken aboard is sufficient.' (Kearton 1930, 97f).

Now the penguin begins to turn into a fish once more. He swallows the stones, hardens and weighs himself down, and becomes a water creature. The moulting period, during which he had to fast and suffer, had given him back to the race of birds. Now the hard stones draw him into the water.

CLIMAXES OF A PENGUIN'S EXISTENCE

What are the high points, the decisive stages, of the penguin's life? Two special experiences are allotted to every penguin. One must be connected with moulting. The condition of distress, illness and fasting remind him of those dark times in which he gave up his existence as a bird and became a fish. For this a yearly penance has been laid upon him — one that all water birds must bear. Is it not remarkable that the penguin does not retreat to pass this period in the dark of his nesting cave? He seeks the companionship of his fellows, as if he sensed that shared suffering is only half-suffering.

Soon after this, however, he eats stones, recapitulating the 'penguin sin'; he becomes a fish, begins to dream, and draws far out into the waters of the ocean.

The other high point is the sight of the newly laid egg. All observers tell with what joy and wonder both parents greet the egg; how they roll it this way and that, look at it from all sides, and simply cannot have enough of it. Is this a sort of intimation of what Rudolf Steiner once said about the form of an egg? (1967, 91 [1921 July 1]).

> The egg is nothing other than a real image of the cosmos . . . philosophers should not speculate about the three dimensions of space, for if one only knows rightly where to look, one finds everywhere the riddles of the world vividly represented. That one axis of the world is longer than the other two — a vivid proof of this is the chicken's egg; its limits — eggshells — are a true picture of our space.

Perhaps an intuitive sense of this knowledge awakens in the penguin parents; they grow to a dawning of this perception. It is this which kindles in them the strength to hatch their egg with the greatest affection and instinctive care, since it has given them this deep experience.

Although penguins on land look so pitiful and ridiculous, the greatness and tragedy of all existence hides under this fool's dress. They are ancestors of man, the penguins; only with them everything is distorted and out of place. For every tragedy has its satire; and so the evolution of man has its clownishness in the being of the penguin.

6 *The purpose of a penguin's existence*

When Brehm tells us that 'we cannot make much ado about the benefit' that penguins bring to man, we must feel that this is a pitiful and mean-spirited way of approaching them. The real question is rather: what is the true sense of their existence?

We must immediately think of the fact that this group of birds inhabits a continent which has remained untouched by man. The Eskimos still live on the edges of the Arctic, but the Antarctic, surrounded by ocean, has never been a human dwelling-place. The living conditions are so inhospitable and hostile that men can exist there only for short periods at great sacrifice.

The penguin, however, has dared to penetrate the dark loneliness and cold of the Antarctic. This alone is a yearly renewed deed of heroism. Particularly the adelie and emperor penguins settle on the high snow and ice-covered plains of the South Pole. Are they not carrying a piece of earthly destiny to this abandoned realm of our planet? Then, when the penguins go back into the sea, having finished their brooding work, they swim out in all directions: to the Falkland Islands near South America, to the Cape of Good Hope, to New Zealand, to Tasmania, thus making a living connection with areas inhabited by human beings.

The penguins link the Antarctic continent with the other regions of the earth by acting as yearly messengers between them. It is not national pacts or territorial demands that they disseminate; they bear tidings of the existence of man on earth to the south polar regions.

Perhaps one day a more exact knowledge of the few existing kinds of penguins will make it possible to assign them to the different races of man, so that they would represent a shadow of all mankind existing on and around the Antarctic continent. Even now the penguins, who mimic man in many caricature-like traits, carry his image to the far frontiers of the earth.

Once the whole world of birds was a mighty spirit that floated, brooding, over the waters. For this reason most kinds of birds can still spread out their wings and fly heavenwards. Others had to renounce flight and commit themselves to earth and water.

The penguins are the apes of the bird family. They also once had wings; but they fell down too quickly into densification, and lost the art of flying. Instead of it they acquired swimming; and now, twice a year, they move from sea to land and back again, proclaiming the song of man to the gloomy South Pole.

It is a crude song, more like the braying of an ass than the song of birds. The penguins caw and quack and purr and bark — and yet their voice sounds from within, calling out into the terrible silence of the polar night: There is life on earth.

The Migrations of Salmon and Eels

1 Migration

Some forty years ago there was great excitement among scientists, particularly among zoologists and palaeontologists, because of a sensational find. Several living specimens of one of the oldest fish in the earth's history, which scientists had assumed to be extinct for about sixty million years, were brought up from the depths of the Indian Ocean. The first one was found on December 22, 1938, but at that time, when the first troubles of the coming war were stirring, not much attention was paid to it. By now (1956) another eight specimens have been fished up. The last one, on November 12, 1954, could even be brought ashore alive and died there since it was not sufficiently protected from the light of the sun.

The name of this ancient group of fish is Coelacanthidae. In spite of the 'struggle for survival' and 'natural selection', they have retained the same form as that of their brothers and sisters found as fossils of the early Mesozoic era, the Triassic period, in Greenland, South Africa, Madagascar and Australia. This discovery not only dealt a perceptible blow to Darwin's theory on the origin of species. What is more important is that living witnesses of a very early period of the earth's evolution reach into the immediate present, with no change in form and mode of living, and thus form a bridge which until now had been thought to have perished.

These eight creatures from the primeval world have come up from the deep seas around Madagascar and South Africa. The next decades will perhaps unveil other such secrets and thus show up how threadbare are many of the views which an agnostic science has formed on the development of organisms. Latimeria — this was the name given to the primeval fish — is only one of the signs, which will be followed by many but has also been preceded by a few. Among them is the deciphering of the mystery of the eels.

Only comparatively recently, during the first two decades of the twentieth century, has a significant light been thrown upon the migration of eels. Already in the nineties of the last century the Italian naturalist Grassi (1854–1925) identified the larval forms of the European eel and showed that the small fish named Leptocephalus which until then had been regarded as a separate species are none other than the larvae from which eels develop. At the beginning of this century the Danish ichthyologist, Johannes Schmidt, took up these leads and in years of most painstaking research found that the Sargasso Sea in the Atlantic Ocean is the common place of origin for both the European and the American eels. It is their cradle and probably also their grave.

Thus a biological phenomenon could be uncovered which until then had seemed scarcely credible. The eels migrate in regular procession, as they go through their larval stages, from the Sargasso Sea right across the Atlantic until they reach the coastal regions of Europe. This move takes about two to three years. Then they go up the rivers, where they grow big and strong, and after a stay of from three to four years return again to the West Indies.

> To the Sargasso Sea!
> Where it is darkest,
> Deepest and darkest,
> There is the goal,
> The beginning and end for us,
> Love and death.

That is how the Dutch poet Albert Verwey (1865–1937)

makes the eels speak. And so it probably is, that 'beginning and end' await them there. But why, after years of wandering through the open seas, do millions upon millions of them go up the rivers? Everything which has been thought about this so far has been all too anthropocentric. For instance that the eels found better living conditions in the rivers, or that they were driven to the place where their 'forebears' had been, and other nonsensical notions. Living conditions in the rivers are much more dangerous and difficult than in the open sea; and what does the word 'dangerous' mean to an animal? What does a thought such as 'better or worse living conditions' mean to an animal? What does it mean to an animal to speak of instinct?

The animal lives embedded in a world of facts and experiences of which it is itself a part, which it does not use to greater or lesser advantage, but within which it fulfils the acts assigned to it by a higher wisdom. An animal is never something which is becoming; man alone is progressing. An animal is always something which is complete in itself and to which a place is given in a definite environment. Within this fixed existence there occurs for thousands of years the self-same act ascribed to this group, family, or species.

The animal acts the role which has been assigned to it for a certain period on the stage of life. Its audience are the gods themselves, who have created this world-theatre out of their own power. Man, too, acts on this stage; but gods watch him, too, and follow his part and sometimes even intervene. But man also beholds his own performance on the stage and knows that he is actor and audience at the same time. The animal is actor only.

Thus Latimeria has now been forced on to the stage of this world-theatre; thus the eels entered the limelight and are now seen particularly clearly. There where earthly and heavenly forces meet and play together, they once, many thousand years ago, made the migrations of eels part of the earth's existence. Now these migrations point back to the evolutionary epoch during which they began. It is there that we should look if we are to gain insight into this strange drama which then appeared in the life of the earth.

But there are all sorts of fishes which migrate; for instance the river-lamprey and sturgeon, salmon and trout; and what has just been said about the eel applies to them all. The salmon, however, show a type of migration and a way of life which is almost the polar opposite of what the eels do. For the salmon, which also travel up rivers and then return to the sea, have their cradle in the head-water region of each river or brook. There the eggs and seed are spread, and the young salmon develop in these places; only thereafter, and at different periods of time, do they go to the open sea. At a later date they travel back to the places of their childhood, where they then produce their own descendants.

The eels therefore go into the sea to produce their progeny, while the salmon go up the rivers to mate. The eels move from the sea to the rivers and back to the sea. The salmon go from the rivers to the sea and back to the rivers. Thus we have a pair of opposite habits, and a study of their contrasting relationships might yield insight into something which until now has remained veiled.

2 Contrasting life cycles

Science has coined two names when describing this polarity; the salmon and all those fishes which rise from the sea into the rivers in order to propagate there are called anadromous, and the contrasting eels, which have their cradle in the sea, catadromous. This designation alone would not help much, unless at the same time a living image were to be gained of the phenomena involved. Sufficient details are known today to give us a fairly complete picture of the patterns of migration.

If we could spend a whole year at the mouth of one of the rivers opening into the North Sea or the Baltic, and were able to observe the fish which move in and out, we should perceive an overwhelming abundance of phenomena. But we must suppose that we could have made our observations in the middle of the last century, when no weirs barred the rivers and no factories destroyed life with effluents.

During autumn time, beginning in October and right through the winter, the salmon rise from the sea and go into the rivers. These are the large, mature males and females, which move up towards the river-heads. In the spring these winter salmon are replaced by the so-called spring salmon, almost all males. They enter the rivers until summer and thereafter a quiet period sets in. In late summer and early autumn a salmon is seldom seen at the river mouth. But even there we get varying rhythms for almost every river. Thus in early summer the St James's salmon go up the River Rhine and the St Bartholomew salmon up the River Elbe — later the larger females follow, and in the autumn the main army of large, heavy salmon ends the procession.

But at the beginning of May, at the mouth of the Rhine, more or less between May 4 and May 18, the young salmon appear, moving in the opposite direction. One to one-and-a-half-years old, they migrate to the sea for the first time. After they have spent their childhood up in the mountains they now go out into the great world. They still wear their youthful dress with dark cross-bands which is only gradually replaced by the silvery splendour of the scales. With them, many of the older salmon, larger and smaller ones, swim and drift out to the open sea; they are returning to the sea after the spawning season, completely exhausted, striving to regain their feeding grounds.

Always, whether they move upstream or downstream, the salmon go singly; they may find themselves in small groups, but as though by accident. With the eels, it is quite different. Coming from the Atlantic, they appear on the west coast of Europe in late winter and during spring — earlier in Ireland and England, and correspondingly later in Denmark, Germany and the Baltic countries. Tens of thousands of small, transparent elvers, 6 to 8 cm (about 3 inches) long, form long columns which move up the rivers. Brehm (1914) quotes an observer, who described it as follows:

> One morning at the end of June or beginning of July, when we went on to the dyke of the village Dreenhausen which looks directly on to the River Elbe, we saw a dark streak which moved along the whole length of the river bank. It was formed by countless numbers of young eels which moved up river near the surface of the water and always kept so close to the bank that they followed all the bends and coves . . . This marvellous procession of fishes continued without interruption or diminution throughout the day and the following day as well.

The eels which go upstream remain in the rivers and brooks for several years and then, having become silver eels, large, darkly pigmented and round, they return to the sea. Mostly in autumn they move back into the open ocean; again this does not happen singly but in smaller and larger processions.

Thus the river mouths become almost throughout the year the gates of entry and exit for billions of fishes which keep up a living communication between the salt water of the sea and the fresh water of the rivers and streams. With tremendous forces both eels and salmon strive up river. To quote Brehm (1914) again:

> At the end of June, I was at Ballyshannon in Ireland at the mouth of the river which in the preceding month had been flooded. Near a cascade it was clouded by millions of small eels which constantly strove to climb the wet rocks on the edges of the

waterfall and died in their thousands; but their damp slippery bodies made a ladder for the others and enabled them to continue on their way. I even saw them climb vertical cliffs; they twisted through the damp moss or got a hold of the bodies of others who had died in the attempt.

Similar, but not so massed, is the upward striving of the salmon. They overcome the greatest obstacles, such as rocks and waterfalls, by flinging themselves from rock ledge to rock ledge, step by step coming closer to their goal.

Eels and salmon move and swim through the entire length and breadth of a river; they enter most of the tribuaries, the streams and streamlets, so that they are intimately interwoven with the whole network of a single river. The eels seem to like broad expanses; the salmon prefer the upper reaches. The river as a biological unit is filled with these fish and through them finds a close connection with the sea.

The life of salmon and eel, however, differs not only in that the one are anadromous and the others catadromous, for this polarity also expresses itself in many individual traits.

The eels stem from the Sargasso Sea, breeding where the Gulf Stream off Florida, coming from the east, turns north and flows along the coast of North America. It is a huge region, almost the whole of which is washed by an arm of the Gulf Stream. The sea is particularly deep there, and from it the young eels rise up. The American species breeds farther to the west, the European one farther to the east of this region. Billions of tiny, transparent, leaf-shaped fish, two to three cm (one inch) long, rise from these depths. Their form is still like a real fish form which, as they approach the western and eastern coasts, increases in size. The migration to Europe, which at the same time means the metamorphosis into elvers, takes two-and-a-half to three-and-a-half years. It is assumed that fertilization takes place in summer, at a depth of two to three thousand metres (7 000–10 000 feet), and that the young larvae gradually rise upwards, grow and — in the course of their eastward migration — change into the round, wormlike elvers. The westward procession is shorter and the American elvers are therefore smaller than the European.

As soon as they have reached the rivers their bodily functions change. A yellowish brown pigment deposits itself in the skin and at the same time there begins a tremendous intake and elimination of substances. During the larval stages the eels do not feed at all, they begin to eat only when moving up the rivers. Then their growth is rapid and they often gain enormously in size and weight. They stay in the fresh water region for three to eight years. During the day they remain hidden in the mud of the river or stream bed and only after dark does their hunting time begin. The eels are active only at night; they fear the daylight. Louis Roule, one of the most knowledgeable ichthyologists, writes (1933, 204f):

> [The eel] is to be numbered with the nocturnal
> creatures of the waters which become active only
> when it is dark. It retains the impression acquired in
> the depths of the sea where it was born . . . If eels
> are kept in an aquarium and a beam of light is
> suddenly brought to bear upon them, they get into
> a panic immediately, dash off in all directions, finally
> piling one on top of another in the darkest corner,
> pressing as close to one another as they can in their
> eagerness to get away from the light they hate . . .
> This persistent, unescapable dread of the light is a
> controlling factor in the life of the eel and makes
> it obvious to us that the eel is indeed a creature of
> the depths.

But it is not only the light that they fear. They withdraw also from the cold and during winter they are inactive; buried in the mud they go through a kind of hibernation.

Among all the river fish they are the first to bury themselves in the autumn and the last to reappear in the spring. Their life-element is dark warmth; cold brightness is the realm from which they flee.

The salmon are quite different. When they rise from the sea into the rivers in autumn their whole body begins to shine. Gerlach (1950) describes it thus: 'As they go up, the salmon change colour. Red spots glow on the gill covers and sides of the males and are also strewn over the bluish shimmering head. The belly turns purple. A rosy pink colours the fins.' Clad in these glorious hues they climb up the river until they have reached the springs of the various tributaries and brooks. They aim for the light and cold in the heights; around and after Christmas, in the ice-cold and light-filled water, mating takes place.

The females pour enormous masses of eggs into a hollow they have prepared beforehand with their fins and the male sperm is shed over these. This mating lasts for one or two weeks and afterwards the exhausted fish make their way to the sea whence they came.

Thus salmon and eels really are polar opposites. Salmon love light and coldness; eels fear them, but love the warm darkness in which the salmon have no part. Both of them link oceans and rivers, salt water and fresh water, and live in the circulatory system of the waters of the earth.

3 The influence of light

The contrast between salmon and eel is also bound up with their different life-elements: the salt water of the sea and the fresh water of the rivers and streams. And how great must be the difference between those generations which have their fertilization and early development high among mountains and hills near the springs, and those who experience this beginning of life in the dark depths of the ocean! It is supposed that eels spawn at a depth of two to three thousand metres (7 000–10 000 feet). If one assumes a thousand metres (3 000 feet) as an average height for the breeding grounds of the salmon, the difference in height between these two beginnings to life is evident.

And the breeding season is deep winter for the salmon, in contrast to high summer for the eels: furthermore, the regions sought by the salmon are northern hills, whilst the Sargasso Sea off Florida belongs to the sub-tropical region.

The eggs of the eel therefore develop in the darkness of salt water, those of the salmon in the light of fresh water. Here far-reaching qualitative differences play a fundamental role in the development of the fish. For sea water not only contains a somewhat larger amount of salts compared with fresh water, but the special composition of its chemical elements deeply influences the organic life which is constantly growing in its womb. The fresh water of the rivers and streams is just the opposite; it is brighter, lighter and quicker, and certainly does not have the brooding character which is so typical of sea water.

Rudolf Steiner once gave a fundamental characterization of this contrast (1952, 11 [1924 Feb 9]):

> Yes, you see, if one really investigates sea-water, one discovers that this salty sea-water stands in but slight connection with the universe. . .
>
> . . . The springs with their fresh water are open to the universe, just as our eyes look freely out into space. We can say therefore that in countries where there are springs, the earth looks far out into the universe; the springs are the earth's sense organs, whereas in the salt ocean we have more the earth's lower body, its bowels . . . And everything through which the earth stands in connection with the cosmos comes from fresh water, everything through which the earth has its intestinal character comes from salt water.

This remark can open up a direct understanding of the phenomena we just described. For it is obvious that the salmon lay their eggs into the 'eyes of the earth', in the springs of rivers and streams and thus right from the start are intimately bound up with the light of the universe. Hence their display of colours, their brightness, their 'salmon-coloured' rosy flesh, their tremendous strength when they move upstream in the rivers. It is the universal light which permeated them and can now live and act in their bodies. They are fish woven from light, and when they move from the hills into the seas, take this light with them and carry it into the wide expanses and depths of the ocean.

The eels, coming from the low-lying regions of the salt water, remain bound to darkness. They are nocturnal animals which flee from the light and strive towards darkness. Colourless, that is, without light, their larvae rise to the surface of the ocean, drift towards the shore, and lose the characteristic fish form in order to metamorphose into the snake-like form. But as soon as they touch fresh water their surface acquires a yellow pigmentation, so that the light of the new surroundings can be reflected. When the eel grows up, it turns into a dark yellow or green water-snake which spends many years in the river. Just as the salmon is exiled to the sea in order to bear its bright light to the depths, so the eel is assigned to the rivers, to bring to them a necessary element of darkness.

But when at the end of its 'river time' the eel returns to the sea and moves homewards, then its eyes begin to grow and the body shows a silvery shine. For now it needs the reflection of light which until then it had shunned. It needs it in order that its sexual organs may acquire the power of reproduction. That which is given to the salmon by the light-filled springs and streams the eel acquires through the enormous enlargement of its eyes. Both need the light so that their progeny may be assured.

THE INFLUENCE OF LIGHT

Rudolf Steiner (1952, 14 [1924 Feb 9]) speaks also of the salmon and describes how necessary it is for these fishes to go up the rivers, in order to get there the celestial forces for their reproductive organs:

> Gravity is the earth-force and works upon everything muscular, everything bony. The earth shares its salt with us and we get strong bones and muscles. With this salt excretion of the earth, however, we could do nothing for our senses and the reproductive organs; they would wither away. These must always come under the influence of extraterrestrial forces, the forces coming from the heavens. And the salmon shows what a distinction it makes between fresh and salt water. It goes into salt water to take up earth forces and get fat.

Thus we gain a more complete picture of the phenomena we are studying. We understand now the polarity at work in the sea and in the rivers and learn to see that the migrations we have described have a meaningful background. They carry the light of the rivers and streams into the darkness of the seas, and the darkness of the ocean into the brightness of the fresh water regions. Eels and salmon are the constant bearers of a form of breathing which makes light and darkness flow to and fro between sea and rivers. From the grotesque deep-sea forms produced by the darkness to the bright vesture of herrings and sprats, trout and minnows — which act almost like arrows of light — brightness and darkness play into each other.

Salmon and eels are taken hold of by this light and darkness; they absorb it and become its messengers.

If the concept we have now gained is fully visualized, we come closer to understanding why a salmon, when it goes up the river, always goes back to the very place where it grew up. At first this was explained as being due to heredity but more recent experiments and observations prove unequivocally that the salmon does not return to the place where its forebears lived, but to where it spent its youth.

Gerlach (1950) reports on breeding experiments in America which prove this most impressively:

In the Columbia river in the north-western United States it has been possible since 1939 to resettle the chinook salmon. These go up the Columbia River. After they have swum 600 km [400 miles] the Grand Coulee Dam now bars their way. It is 180 m [600 feet] high and the water in the reservoir above is too warm for the salmon. In 1939 the Federal Fish and Wildlife Service, under the direction of Dr Ira Gabrielson, began to catch the salmon 120 km (75 miles) below the Grand Coulee Dam as they came up the fish ladders and to take them in big tank wagons to the breeding station at Leavenworth, where the eggs were artificially fertilized. When the hatched fry were big enough to use their fins they were taken in tank wagons to the upper reaches of the Wenatches, Eutiat, Okanagon and Methow rivers and put out there. These rivers flow into the Columbia river below the Grand Coulee Dam. The young chinook salmon remained there until after one year they had reached a length of about 15 cm [6 inches]. They then drifted down to the ocean and were seen no more. They should have reappeared in 1944 to spawn, five years after they were born. And they did it. When they were small they had been marked by cuts in their fins. Those which had been placed in the Wenatches took without hesitation the way to this river, and the salmon from the Eutiat, Okanagon and Methow were equally sure in finding again the place where they had grown up. The home of their parents — above the Grand Coulee Dam — they did not seek any more. The same procedure was used in later seasons, and the resettlement experiment was successful.

THE INFLUENCE OF LIGHT

This indicates precisely the strange ability of the salmon to find their way back to the place of their origin, the fountain of their youth, after many years of travel which must take them thousands of miles. To write off such an ability as 'instinct' would be dodging the issue. Heredity cannot play any role in it either; it is a different principle which can be conjectured. The fish cannot 'find' the way; they have neither the sensory nor the discerning faculties for such a complex ability. The only possible consideration is that they move 'blind', but 'blind' in the sense that aeroplanes can fly 'blind', because they are under remote control. It is only when we begin to imagine that every single salmon remains linked to the special light of the place of its youth, and that a delicate beam of this light accompanies it on all its travels, invisible to the human eye but perceptible to the salmon, that one comes closer to a first understanding of this strange phenomenon. Like the two children in the fairy tale who drop breadcrumbs on their path through the thick forest so that they can find the way home again, the salmon leaves small threads of light behind in the sea, so that even years later it can follow them back to its place of origin.*

To me it looks almost as if the millions of salmon which every year descend from the rivers into the darkness of the sea carry these flickers and threads of light with them and thereby gently lighten the darkness of the ocean. When they return to their river they roll this thread of light up again and use it for the colours of their wedding garment. This concept can be borne out if one remembers the many different deep sea fish which are equipped with absurd little lanterns and lights on all sorts of parts of their bodies. In their case these sources of light are visible also to the human eye, because these fish do not spawn high up at the springs and thus receive the invisible light

---

* It is now known that salmon find their home river by their sense of smell (*Editor*).

in the form of light-ether as their endowment at birth. The deep-sea fish have to create these light sources from within their bodies and thus it becomes coloured light which glimmers but is not able to shine.

A similar riddle is provided by the eels, which in their migrations find the rivers and on their return never miss the Sargasso Sea. Here again 'blind' swimming can provide a plausible explanation. The eels come from the dark depths and rise to the surface of the sea as transparent larvae floating towards the European or American shores. In their nursery, however, no distinction is made between American and European larvae: the two grow up together and yet every single larva 'knows' where it belongs. So some float westward, the others eastward.

If one were to speak of instinct one would again only obscure the issue. But it can be visualized that both the European and American rivers radiate a very delicate light into the darkness of the sea and that different light qualities shine from the East and from the West. Almost the only difference between the American eel larvae and the European is that the first have fewer vertebrae: the former have between 103 and 110, while the latter have between 111 and 119 (Roule 1933, 200). It is perhaps possible that the spine acts as a very delicate antenna which draws one group to the west and the other to the east.

In such problems of animal life one must not overlook the environment and its wide differentiations. Its manifold forces act upon the animal which has been created out of them and for them. An eel larva is almost nothing but a complex sensory organ and only when it changes into the rounded form of the elver does it develop an additional digestive and metabolic organization. Thus the 'light antenna' — the early larva — is guided in the direction from which the light which it is able to perceive is shining. Near the river this light trail becomes so strong that the skin becomes pigmented and the animal metamorphoses into a feeding organism.

THE INFLUENCE OF LIGHT

Years later, when the fully matured eel again travels from the river into the sea, the eye begins to grow; for now the eel returns to its dark homeland and again turns into a sense organ. Now it ceases to eat and yearns for the darkness whence it has come. Both salmon and eel spend their lifetime in a constant interplay of light and darkness.

Thus we can understand what Rudolf Steiner once said so vividly about the nature of fishes (1970, 110f [1923 Oct 28]):

> The fish has water within it, yet the fish does not feel itself as the water; the fish feels itself to be what encloses the water, what surrounds the water. It feels itself to be the glittering sheath or vessel enclosing the water. But the water itself is felt by the fish as an element foreign to it, which passes out and in, and, in doing so, brings the air which the fish needs. Yet air and water are felt by the fish as something foreign. In its physical nature the fish feels the water as something foreign to it. But the fish has also its etheric and astral body. And it is just this which is the remarkable thing about the fish; because it really feels itself to be the vessel, and the water this vessel encloses remains connected with all the rest of the watery elements, the fish experiences the etheric as that in which it actually lives. It does not feel the astral as something belonging to itself.
>
> Thus the fish has the peculiar characteristic that it is so entirely an etheric creature. It feels itself as the physical vessel for the water. It feels the water within itself as part and parcel with all the waters of the world. Moisture is everywhere, and in this moisture the fish at the same time experiences the etheric. For earthly life fishes are certainly dumb, but if they could speak and could tell you what they feel, then they would say: 'I am a vessel, but the

vessel contains the all-pervading elements of water, which is the bearer of the etheric element. It is in the etheric that I am really swimming.' The fish would say: 'Water is only Maya; the reality is the etheric, and it is in this that I really swim.' Thus the fish feels its life as one with the life of the earth. This is the peculiar thing about the fish: it feels its life as the life of the earth, and therefore it takes an intimate part in everything which the earth experiences during the course of the year, experiencing the outgoing of the etheric forces in summer, the drawing-back of the etheric forces in winter. The fish experiences something which breathes in the whole earth. The fish perceives the etheric element as the breathing process of the earth.

Here Steiner describes the extraordinarily subtle sensory world of the fishes; as sensory antennae they perceive the breathing of the earthly ether-world. The eels and salmon are embedded in this ether realm; they swim in the water; but they live in the etheric flow of light and darkness, of warmth and cold, of sound and chemical activity, of living and dying.

Therefore the salmon are connected to the course of the year as a sundial is to the progress of the day. In the autumn, when the earth-ether is inhaled, they go up to their springs, to spawn at the time of midwinter. In the spring they migrate into the sea, in close connection with the exhaling stream of the earth's ether.

Thus too the eels return to the sea in autumn, to spawn in the Sargasso Sea at midsummer and then to die.

Both species of fish live in the interplay of light and dark which continually recurs between the sea and the rivers, between salt water and fresh water, between the cosmic forces and the depths of the earth.

4 The spiritual evolution of salmon and eels

Since Johannes Schmidt made the important discovery that the Sargasso Sea is the breeding place of the European and American eels, many scientists have given much thought to the problem why this happens just there and nowhere else. More and more it was seen in connection with Wegener's theory of continental drift and today a group of scientists assume that the eels were once fresh-water fish which — as it were — fell into the sea as the European and American continents gradually separated.

Muir-Evans (1943, 87), for instance, describes how the Afro-European land mass separated from the American block and then writes:

> If this is correct one can visualize the larva of the European eel as originally ascending eastern rivers which were quite handy, but as the continents became separated the journey of the larva to its fresh water would gradually be extended until a journey of three thousand miles [5 000 km] intervened. It is difficult to think geologically but this theory alone gives reasonable explanation of the migration of the European eel.

Eugen Kraus too tried to solve this problem (1932). He was the first one who pointed out that the migrations of the eels seem to be connected with the Gulf Stream. He thinks that Rudolf Steiner's statement that the Gulf Stream once flowed around the Atlantean continent may help in the solution of this important riddle.

However, if Rudolf Steiner's indications are studied accurately, the former Atlantean continent does not in any way come near the region of the Sargasso Sea of to-day. For the statement reads (1970, 161f [1910 June 16]):

> This continent was encircled by a warm stream which, strange as it may seem, was seen clairvoyantly to flow from the South through Baffin Bay towards the North of Greenland, encircling it.

Then, turning eastward, it gradually cooled down.
Long before the continents of Russia and Siberia
had emerged, it flowed past the Ural mountains,
changed course, skirted the Eastern Carpathians,
debouched into the region now occupied by the
Sahara and finally reached the Atlantic Ocean in
the neighbourhood of the Bay of Biscay . . . This
stream is the Gulf Stream which at that time
encircled the Atlantean continent.

This shore-line of the old Atlantis, the centre of which
was roughly in the region where Ireland lies today, leaves
the Sargasso Sea far outside its boundary.

The distribution of the eels, however, runs only parti-
ally parallel to this shore-line. Kraus himself says (1932):

The European eel therefore appears on all European
coasts, along Scandinavia up to the White Sea and
in the Baltic Sea, in the Mediterranean and on the
north coast of Africa, in the Black Sea, from the
Sea of Marmara to the Sea of Azov, and finally to
Iceland (except on the north and north-east coast).

The American eel settles in the eastern regions of
North America up to Labrador, in south-west
Greenland, the north coast of the Gulf of Mexico,
the eastern edge of the Caribbean including the
Bahamas, the Greater and Lesser Antilles, down to
the Mouths of the Orinoco on the north-east coast
of South America.

This delineates the region in which the eels migrate
today, but it is very different from what was once the
outline of Atlantis in the way described by Rudolf
Steiner. It may well be that the eels did once go up the
rivers of Atlantis and that, as that continent gradually
subsided, they gradually moved to other coastal regions.
But the Sargasso Sea must have been the uterus of the
eels since primeval epochs, long before even Atlantis
existed. They are fishes and thus belong to the most
ancient days of the earth.

THE SPIRITUAL EVOLUTION

They have, however, retained their peculiar metamorphosis from fish to the form of a snake, similar to the developmental stages of the frog and other amphibians which still show their origin from fishes as tadpoles. This transformation of the larva of the eel into its snake-like form is no doubt a pointer to very ancient bodily changes to which this creature must have been subjected.

Anyone who has studied Rudolf Steiner's spiritual science in relation to earth-evolution can hardly doubt that this transformation of the eels occurred during the period when humanity experienced the Fall of man. It is the same period during which the moon separated itself from the earth thus making other steps in the course of evolution possible.

Like all other fishes, the eels must have their archetypal origin in the Hyperborean age, during a time when sun and earth were still one heavenly body, permeated with light and warmth. But when the sun separated from the earth, the fishes were born as animal beings. Rudolf Steiner indicates this (1955, 100f [1908 Aug 11]):

[Man] had only a very fine etheric form at the time when the earth and sun were still united. When these separated he thrust from him certain animal forms, and these have remained behind at the stage in evolution which corresponds to the time when the sun was still within the earth. From these, entirely different forms have naturally arisen in the course of time . . . Were we to select a characteristic form which is still to be found today, and which may in some way be compared with those which remained behind when the earth was thrust away by the sun, we must select the form of the fish . . . it is that which still has within it the last echo of the Sun-Forces.

This throws a first but very important light on the evolution of the fishes, showing that they must be counted among the oldest earthly organisms. It is from this primeval time that Latimeria has survived unchanged until our day. Other fishes, probably most of them, underwent further evolution and the metamorphosis of the eel from a tiny fish into a kind of snake is but *one* instance of such transformations.

In the same lecture Rudolf Steiner said (1955, 104):

. . . when the sun separated from the earth, the earth went back in development; it degenerated; and only after the moon withdrew with the worst constituents did improvement again take place. There was, therefore, for some time an ascending development until the departure of the sun; then a descending one, when everything became worse, more grotesque; then, after the moon withdrew, a re-ascending development again.

From this stage of evolution we have also a form which has degenerated, and which does not by any means appear now as it did then, but it exists; it is the form which belonged to man before the moon withdrew, before he had an ego. The animal form which recalls the lowest stage of earthly development, the time when man plunged most deeply into passions and when his astral body was susceptible to the worst external influence, is that of the serpent . . .

The eel has retained this form and it is still possible to follow the changes which lead from the form of the fish to the form of the snake, via the elver to the yellow eel and to the shining black eel. The eel is like a living memorial which has been preserved to remind us of that period when the form of the snake developed into the reptiles of today.

Since that time, too, the eels have become carriers of poisonous substances. Their blood and body fluids have a paralysing and lethal action on other organisms. This is a remnant of that lowest point in earth evolution of which Steiner speaks.

THE SPIRITUAL EVOLUTION

In the legends and myths of the peoples of Madagascar, Australia, the Philippines and the South Sea Islands, eels play a great role. The souls of the dead live in them and ancestors are even called eels. This is a region inhabited by a large eel family. Kraus writes (1932):

> There are nineteen species, three of which belong to the temperate zones and the other sixteen to the tropical zone. In the northern temperate zone is found the Japanese eel, which is strikingly similar to the Atlantic species and therefore stands out clearly among the other Indo-Pacific species.

Here, where once the moon left the earth and where the Lemurian continent lay, is another eel region perhaps as important as the Atlantic one. It is not yet known where in the Indian or Pacific Oceans lies the breeding place of these Lemurian eels which would correspond to the Sargasso Sea. But that it is to be found in the very region where the metamorphosis from fish into eel occurred is significant, and Kraus was the first to indicate this emphatically.

The salmon, however, has remained free from this world of the Fall. It lives in the light of the springs, where it has its youth, and moves from there to the sea as a bearer of light. It is a true fish which points back to that Hyperborean time when sun and earth were still one. A remnant of the brightness which permeated that earth epoch still lives in the salmon today. The area of its distribution is quite different from that of the eel. Brehm writes (1914):

> The home of the salmon must be taken to be the waters of the temperate region of Europe, southwards down to a latitude of 43°N, and of the New World down to 41°N. This fish is absent from all the rivers which run into the Mediterranean. In Germany it visits chiefly the Rhine and its tributaries, the Oder and the Weichsel [now Wisla in Poland], though it is not absent from the Elbe

and Weser. It is found more frequently in the rivers of Great Britain, Russia, Scandinavia, Iceland, Greenland and North America, more rarely in those of western France and the north of Spain.

This means a belt which envelops almost the entire Arctic region. Like a ribbon spread around the North Pole the salmon live in both the Old and the New Worlds. And thus they have remained faithful to the region in which they first arose. The Hyperborean region was where the salmon are today, in the north, where light and cold act in a direct way upon the earth's surface.

The salmon has remained faithful to the sun. When this great star separated from the earth, the salmon followed it by rising from the sea upstream into the northern rivers, higher and higher towards the light of the sun, so that at the furthermost point, where the springs become the 'eyes of the earth', it could be closest to its creator. There it performs the sacrificial deed of procreation and its young remain for more than one year devoted to the realm of light.

The eels, on the other hand, followed the path of the earth. They went down to the depths of the Atlantic and Indian Oceans and thus left the light and became the sons of darkness. Hence they had to transform into snakes and become bearers of the darkness. The eels came under the forces of the moon, and are still ruled by her today as they were once upon a time. Their colour is yellow and greenish, similar to that of the waxing moon. Like the invisible new moon they rise from the depths as transparent and insignificant forms, increase in strength and travel up into the rivers. But even there the eel remains a nocturnal animal, in thrall to the moon.

Both salmon and eel are fish. But the one has remained a pure fish and thus a son of the sun; the other has developed further, become a scion of the moon and taken on the destiny of the snake. Yet they are brothers; they know of each other and one day, when the end of the earth has come, they will return together and become children of God.

At the end of the Sermon on the Mount (Matt.7:9,10), Christ says: 'Or what man of you, if his son ask him for bread, will give him a stone? Or if he asks for a fish, will give him a serpent?'

In these words from the New Testament lives the statement which shows fish and snake, salmon and eel, in their mutual relation as brothers. Rudolf Steiner brings all this together when he said (1955, 104 [1908 Aug 11]):

Fish and snake symbols are derived from the mysteries of our evolution. It is quite natural for a person to experience a feeling of pleasure when he sees the glistening body of a fish in the pure, chaste water element; it gives him a feeling of peace; just as to those of a pure disposition it gives a feeling of horror to see a creeping snake. Such feelings are by no means meaningless memories of things once passed through.

The witnesses of this are the salmon and eels. They are the living witnesses of a past and yet extant world which to our senses is hardly perceptible, but can be revealed by imaginative understanding. It is the sphere wherefrom all living beings arise; that kingdom where the powers of light and darkness weave and flow and are the fountain-head of all creatures.

Year after year the teeming eel larvae rise from the depths of the Sargasso Sea and the Indian Ocean; the ocean transforms its creatures from fishes into snakes and then calls them back again.

Opposite to this welling up from the depths are the thousands of springs of northern rivers, streams and brooks in America, Europe and Asia. There billions of eggs of the salmon — spread out in a huge circle around the globe — are annually hatched by the light; from the periphery the young salmon move to the centre around the Arctic Sea.

Here are two circulations which stand opposite each other: one begins in the centre and the other in the periphery; one bears light, the other darkness. Interweavingly they maintain the circulation of all the waters which are filled with light and darkness.

And there is no thing in nature
Which has been created or born
Which does not reveal its inner
form externally.
                    (Jakob Böhme)

Dolphins — Children of the Sea

1 Contemporary interest

Anyone who has seen and observed dolphins can hardly escape from their fascination. They convey a feeling of contentment and joy. Some years ago a dolphin appeared at Opononi, a small place on the North Island of New Zealand, and made friends with the children and fishermen who lived there. Soon thousands of visitors came to watch the sociable animal at play (Alpers 1960, 136f):

> Some people got so excited when they saw Opo
> . . . that they went into the water fully clothed, just
> to touch her . . . In the evenings, when it was too
> chilly to be in the water any longer and the dolphin
> had gone off, everyone talked about her. In the tents
> . . . the campers exchanged their scanty knowledge
> of the marvel, speaking in low voices while the
> children slept. They visited each other's tents,
> becoming friends with total strangers in an instant,
> all because of the dolphin . . . There was such an
> overflow of these friendly feelings that it seemed the
> crowds were composed of people wanting to be
> forgiven . . .

Similar stories are known from antiquity. Herodotus, Pliny, Phylarchos and many other Greek and Roman writers record remarkable meetings and experiences with dolphins, describing their friendship with children and young men, and their helpfulness and self-sacrifice in saving those who are drowning.*

---

* Recently four Japanese fishermen, whose boat capsized about 50 km

In the legends of Greece and Rome there are many stories of dolphins; they appear on coins, cups, jars, grave-stones and mosaics. At no other time have they been so present to human consciousness. (Rabinovitch 1947, Urner 1959).

Aristotle wrote in his *History of the Animals* much about dolphins (Book 9, ch. 35):

> Among the sea-creatures, many stories are told about the dolphin, indicative of his gentle and kindly nature, and of manifestations of devoted affection for boys, in and about Tarentum, Caria, and other places. The story goes that after a dolphin had been caught and wounded off the coast of Caria, a school of dolphins came into the harbour in response to his cries and stopped there until the fisherman let his captive go free; whereupon the school departed. A school of young dolphins is always, by way of protection, followed by a large one. On one occasion a school of dolphins, large and small, was seen, and two dolphins at a little distance appeared swimming in underneath a little dead dolphin when it was sinking, and supporting it on their backs. . . .

From these and similar observations (Alpers 1960, Slijper 1962), it can be seen that these animals have not only a special relationship to human beings, but also live in close relationship and co-operation with one another. It seems to be one of their characteristics that they show helpfulness to others; something rare among animals, which deserves close study. What are the dolphins, and what is their origin?

(30 miles) from the coast, were rescued by dolphins. Each carried two men on its back to the shore. This story was told by the fishermen themselves. (*Tier*, 1964, Jan. Vol. 3, No. 1).

2 The whale family

The dolphins and porpoises all belong to a larger group of mammals which live in the seas and in some rivers. They are included in the order of whales (*Cetacea*). The suborders are distinguished: the toothed whales (*odontoceti*) and the baleen or whalebone whales (*mysticeti*).

The former have as their name indicates fully developed mandibles. The baleen whales, however, have no teeth; they have in their mouths great racks, in which the small creatures which they eat are caught.

The baleen whales are the largest animals now living, among them the blue whale and the fin whale which are hunted in the oceans of the Arctic and Antarctic. They are mysterious creatures, whose behaviour and way of life are still obscure. Their migrations, their appearance and disappearance are only partly known. For millennia they have been attacked and exploited by men; but their mystery has not yet been revealed.

Very different are the *odontoceti*. Among them there are giants too, like the sperm whale and the white whale. Both of these are much exploited, for they are often not much smaller than the mighty baleen whales. But they all have teeth; the sperm whale, however, only on the lower jaw. There is also a strange group, the narwhals, which have generally only one gigantic tooth which projects from the upper jaw as a spiral horn two or three yards long.

Several of the *odontoceti* are fierce robbers, which rend and kill any creature that they meet. There is the fearful killer whale, with a dorsal fin projecting upwards like a mighty dagger. A Danish biologist, Eschricht, in the last century found in one of these creatures which had been caught and killed, the still fresh bodies of thirteen porpoises and fourteen seals. The fifteenth seal had stuck in the throat of this monster and suffocated it (Slijper 1962, 274).

71

The small porpoise, *Phocaena*, lives particularly in the northern waters of the Atlantic and sometimes swims up the great rivers — the Rhine, the Elbe and the Thames. There seems to be no difficulty for the *odontoceti* to change from salt water to fresh. Even killers have been observed and caught in rivers.

The dolphins themselves inhabit particularly the seas of the northern hemisphere, but are well-known too on the coasts of Australia and New Zealand; in these regions the large bottle-nosed dolphins with which the present investigations in America are concerned are found.

This short and incomplete survey nevertheless gives a first picture of the whales. According to the present results of research it appears to be justified to regard the *mysticeti* as having their home more in the Arctic and Antarctic regions, and the *odontoceti* nearer to the equator. The river dolphins whose snouts are extended in a beak-like form are found particularly in equatorial countries, for example in the Ganges and the Brahmaputra, and related forms in the Amazon and the Orinoco. Only *odontoceti* live in the rivers, and these in the temperate and equatorial regions. The *mysticeti* inhabit the seas round the Arctic and Antarctic circles. The *mysticeti* which have a longer history on earth live nearer to the polar zones; the *odontaceti* which appear later approach the equator. The two orders however overlap considerably in their geographical distribution; nevertheless this general scheme appears to be correct.

3 The dolphin's life in water

One characteristic belongs to both groups: they are given up entirely to life in the water. The seals, *Pinnipedia*, still change from the sea to the land and back to the water again. These mate and breed on the land, and the calves have to learn to swim and hunt in water. But the whales are entirely confined to the water; they do not return to land at any stage of their lives. Only if the sea throws them upon the coast, and they are unable to get back into the water because of injury or the retreating tide, they are connected indeed with the solid earth but this is then their grave. They are much more definitely creatures of the water than the seals; in spite of their mammalian nature they have left the dry land entirely. The seas and rivers have become their pastures.

Their bodies have become more closely fitted to life in the water than those of the seals. For example, they have no hind-legs. Only rudimentary pelvic bones have remained and prove that rear limbs once existed. The arms too have atrophied and changed into two fins, which are used for guiding their movements, not for propulsion. And most *odontoceti* have developed a large dorsal fin, which the seals lack. They have thus many characteristics in which they resemble fishes. But the tail has a fundamental difference. This is not vertical as in the real fishes, but horizontal with some detachment and freedom from the backbone. It impels the animal like a propeller with a quick and powerful rotating movement which its position makes possible. All forward movement comes about in this way. Dolphins easily achieve a speed of twenty knots (37 km/h).

In their movements these animals are great artists. They are not only fast swimmers, who can race with any large ocean steamer, but also tremendous jumpers and divers, often hopping over small sailing boats as if to tease their crews. They can leap for yards out of the water and dive in again gracefully and easily. Their moving games are varied, and much more agile than those of the seals.

In their games they can balance balls on their snouts, throw motor tyres, and catch objects. In the Marineland Institute at Miami, Florida, dolphins can be observed playing with the feathers of water birds; they let these be carried away by the currents in the large tank, pursue them, and bring them back. They can carry human beings as riders on their backs through the water, showing both the speed and the steady balance of the movement. No fish could do this. All dolphins live in herds; they are very seldom to be found alone; even when they make friends with human beings, they are often accompanied by another dolphin. As has been mentioned, they help each other when one of them is wounded or in need.

Alpers (1960) tells how some years ago seven dolphins were stranded on a small island in the north of New Zealand. They were seven or eight feet long, and the holiday-makers (friends of Alpers, who told him what happened) made every effort to drag them back into the sea. This energetic rescue attempt was however a failure, because of the community feeling among the group; for directly one of the seven was in the water, he attempted with all his power to join his stranded companions. None of them was willing to leave the others in their need. After many hours of effort, two dolphins were rescued; the remainder died on the shore; their sense of community did not allow them to preserve their own lives when the others were losing theirs.

Behaviour of this kind is only found otherwise among birds and mammals when they have their young. Then the mothers sacrifice themselves to preserve the life of their offspring. For this to happen on behalf of every member of the herd, as with the dolphins, is unique.

Lilly (1962, 36) reports the following occurrence:

> An animal that was being delivered to an oceanarium struck his head on the side of the pool as he was being let into it. He was knocked unconscious and dropped to the bottom. The other dolphins pushed him to the surface and held him there until he began to breathe again.

There are many similar observations. A mother dolphin holds her offspring on the surface until it has drawn the first breath. For the birth takes place, as mating does, under water.

We are thus dealing with mammals which are given up entirely to life in the water, but which always have to come to the surface to breathe. All whales, *odontoceti* as well as *mysticeti*, can only live in water if it is always possible for them to breathe air. This happens at very different intervals and under very different conditions. It is stated that dolphins come up at intervals of three to five minutes in order to breathe in fresh air and breathe out used air. They then breathe very quickly, exchanging each time five to ten litres of air.

4 *The senses of dolphins*

From this description it is clear that the organ which enables air to be breathed in and out is, for dolphins and whales, the centre of their life. This is the blow-hole at the top of the head. It consists of a small hole which can be opened and closed by a valve. The muscles of this complicated apparatus are arranged in such a way that it is opened actively, and closed passively. This hole is like a pupil for the air, actively opened outside water and drawn together passively when the dolphin dives.

This central point at the top of the head should not be compared with the crown of the head in the human being. For only behind the blow-hole does the bony cover of the skull begin, within which the brain is embedded. This place could only be compared in the human face with the region at the root of the nose. But the dolphin lacks the external nose entirely, and only remnants of the inner nasal passages are preserved in the neighbourhood of the blow-hole. What appears like a nose is the upper jaw, cushioned with fat and oil. From the blow-hole an airway leads down vertically through the upper jaw into the complicated larynx. From this the inbreathed air proceeds through a short passage into the branching bronchial

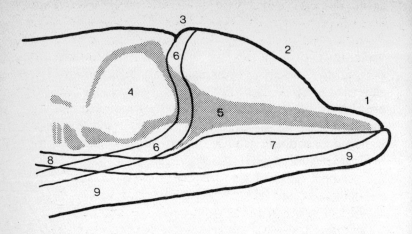

1. Rostrum	4. Brain	7. Interior of mouth
2. Upper jaw	5. Bone of upper jaw	8. Food passage
3. Blowhole	6. Airway	9. Lower jaw

Section through the head of a bottle-nosed dolphin (after Lilly 1962)

tubes of the lungs. The apparatus for closing the blow-hole and the air passage leading to it is a system of valves and rings, which can be opened and closed independently at various places.

Immediately below the blow-hole the air passage widens into two larger and two smaller air reservoirs, arranged symmetrically. These air reservoirs, which surround the air passage and are enclosed in a thick net of muscles, serve for the production of sound, which can be achieved both under water and in the air. The larynx too not only regulates the stream of breath, but can probably produce sounds under water. It is now certain that dolphins can communicate through the most varied sounds. These consist of a deep creaking sound, and notes which extend over grunts and whistles into frequencies which are inaudible to us. These are emitted in the presence of danger and to call other dolphins to help. (The seven dolphins which were stranded, as was described above, communicated through these high frequencies.)

Further, dolphins emit another kind of supersonic wave: this works on the principle of echo location. Solid objects in the water — for example single fish, shoals, ships and rocks — are tested by these sound waves, which are thrown back and perceived as a sense impression by the dolphins. (Norris and others 1961). These supersonic signals are sent out abruptly and in various rhythms (Lilly 1962, 73):

> Apparently it [this sonar system] can be used to determine not only the distance and direction of an object but its form as well; by this technique they can find a fish that they want to eat and distinguish it from other objects.

It is probable that the entire surface of the body is sensitive to these reflected sound waves. For the skin is specially fine and smooth and nevertheless as if invulnerable. For when a wound is caused, from the lower fat layer an oil penetrates into it which stops the bleeding and closes and covers the opening.

No single hair is to be found on the skin of the dolphin, not even bristles or moustaches on the face. Everything is smooth and shining, perhaps in order to make the perception involved in echo location as clear as possible.

Through the special position of the blow-hole and air passage the nose has atrophied. The entire loss of the organ of smell and the two olfactory nerves is connected with this. We have to suppose that no smell of any kind is observed by dolphins, when they draw breath on the surface of the water. It is still in doubt whether they have a sense of taste.

But one sense organ is very highly developed; the ear. Although it is hardly visible externally, as its position is only indicated by a tiny opening behind the eye, and although the outer auditory canal is very long, narrow, and bent in the form of an S — the middle and inner ear are developed with great complexity. The bone which contains them is specially hard — the hardest of all bones found in animals. This is not, as with man and most mammals, grown together with the skull, but only connected with it by ligaments and muscles. In this way it becomes possible for this ear bone (*petrosum*) to be moved in many directions and to adapt itself to a particular sound.

The real inner ear, the cochlea, is much larger in dolphins than in man. It has two convolutions and is particularly developed in the lower part which is connected with the perception of high notes. The auditory nerves connected with this organ are also much more powerfully developed than in man. If one considers that the capacity for perception for high and very high notes is very much greater in dolphins than in other mammals including man then the special development of the whole ear can be understood. Human beings can distinguish notes lying approximately between 20 cycles and 20 kilocycles. With whales and dolphins, but particularly with the latter, this sensitivity rises to 140 kilocycles.

Thus the dolphin, and probably most other whales, are a group of animals with a quite special capacity of hearing. They perceive their environment especially through sounds, notes and noises. Their realm is not resounding air but the reverberating water. They breathe air but they experience their watery environment as a sounding and rippling, as the resounding of the breakers, the steady murmur of the waves.

Is it astonishing that the Greeks associated the dolphin both with Dionysus blowing his flute and with Apollo, the master of music? That they let the dolphins play to the sound of the lyre?

5 The brain

Another special characteristic of all dolphins, porpoises, and other whales, is the exceptional development of their brain. No other mammal, not even the anthropoid apes, can be compared with them. In absolute and relative size of brain the *odontoceti* are the only mammals which are close to man.

That such mighty creatures as the baleen whales should have enormous brains is not surprising. These weigh about 7 kg (15 or 16 lb). But dolphins and porpoises not much larger than man have about the same size of brain, which is an extraordinary phenomenon.

In addition, the form, structure and convolutions of the dolphin brain are remarkably similar to that of man. The former, indeed, appears as if compressed at the back; but it is not much behind the construction of our brain in the complexity of its development. The convolutions and folds are very numerous, and recent investigations have shown that the number of nerve cells is similar to that of the human brain substance. The same must be said of the cerebellum, in every respect. It is not only large, but complex and similar to that of man.

Among the nerves of the brain the olfactory nerve is missing, being only present in a rudimentary form in some baleen whales. The visual nerve too is relatively small. Only the auditory nerve is outstanding in size. It is much the most highly developed sense nerve, and in connection with it those parts of the cerebrum which are connected with hearing are particularly well developed. Here too is shown the nature of the dolphin which is so deeply concerned with the realm of sound.

But why is the brain so large, and so human in form? This has become a burning question to those who have occupied themselves with this matter. Lilly and other researchers in North America chose the bottle-nosed dolphin as the object of their experiments because they assumed that the size of brain should permit communication like that of speech. Lilly, for example, is convinced that the capacity of speech is bound to a definite size of brain and that the growing child can only learn to express itself through speech when the necessary size of brain has been reached around the second year.

Such considerations certainly deserve to be treated with a certain scepticism. But the question remains: why have dolphins and other *odontoceti* such a highly developed brain? Many researchers bring this into connection with their skilful capacity for movement; others (Crile and Quirnig) believe that the particularly active metabolic system is responsible. But where there are such varied possibilities of explanation the real answer has not yet been found.

In this connection the astonishingly mature social behaviour of the dolphins is to be considered, which has been already described; the strong connection they have with one another and their amiability towards humans. It must be remembered that dolphins behave quite differently, for example, towards fish. It is known that fishermen in various regions are assisted by dolphins. They summon them with high-pitched whistles; and the dolphins drive shoals of fish towards the boats, as hunting dogs drive game towards hunters. Pliny describes this behaviour; so does Oppianus, a great admirer of the dolphins. In our times similar observations have been made (Slijper 1962). Dolphins behave with particular enmity towards sharks. They attack them by driving their closed jaws into the body of the shark and tearing open the wound made in this way with their sharp teeth, of which they have eighty-eight. But a human being has never been chased or attacked.

Lilly's assertion that he has never seen a sleeping dolphin is important (1962, 36):

Because they do not constantly have to resist gravity as we do, they do not need to sleep as we do. As we discovered, they cannot afford deep unconsciousness at all from any cause — anaesthesia, epileptic convulsions, or a blow on the head hard enough to produce unconsciousness will kill them.

This can be understood if one remembers that all whales have to come to the surface to breathe at shorter or longer intervals. If this does not happen they are doomed. Is this perhaps the reason for the size of their brain — that it protects them from falling asleep, that different parts of the cerebral cortex can be active in turn, while parts that have been exhausted by consciousness can recover?

How otherwise can this continuous consciousness be achieved? There are many riddles here waiting to be answered. But does not the ever-waking dolphin bring into the depths of the ocean an element which can be felt like an illumination of the water? Fishes have a dim, dream-like consciousness. Whales however carry their constant day-consciousness down into the depths of the ocean, bringing light into the darkness ruling there.

6 *The essence of the dolphin*

To bring all these phenomena into a single, inclusive and comprehensive picture, revealing the nature and development of the dolphins, is a difficult undertaking. Is it right yet to attempt any such picture, tentatively or definitely?

We picture the oceans of the earth, through which there wander the mighty baleen whales; like memorials of a primeval age they plough the waters in the polar regions, grazing on the billions of small creatures which form their food. They are joined towards the tropics by the toothed whales; from the mighty sperm-whale to the fierce killers, and the schools of dolphins and porpoises. For all these, although they are mammals, life in the water has been prescribed by world destiny. They have continually to come up from the depths in order to breathe in and out, and this demands uninterrupted wake-fulness; sleep and every other form of loss of consciousness bring death. Therefore their brain is specially large and has as complex folds as that of man. The nose is turned upwards, so that its opening, transformed into a blow-hole, comes to lie at the top of the head.

In this way mouth and nose, which are otherwise among mammals closely connected, are anatomically separated. Between them an unoccupied space has remained which gives to all whales and particularly to dolphins their peculiar facial form. The widely spaced eyes survey this empty field of the upper jaw. High up breath is expelled and inhaled. The clear separation between nourishment and breathing is a particular characteristic of the whales. Through the blow-hole which points upwards they have given to breathing a special place. For them it must be similar in character to the human capacity for forming mental pictures. For whales have no rhythmic breathing process, as have most of the other animals; their breathing is dependent upon consciousness, upon the varying circumstances of their lives, upon the struggle and the joyful game of existence.

Furthermore the sense of smell has been lost by them. Wherever the power of smell decreases, it is transformed into another capacity. Rudolf Steiner (1983 [1920 Oct 3]) once described how the loss of that powerfully developed sense of smell which exists among the animals, leads in man to the development of the intellect. Thus the human face is not extended forwards as in the face of many ruminants, beasts of prey, and apes, but pointing steeply upwards and downwards, granting space to the brow and the chin.

But where did the transformed sense of smell go in the dolphin? Here it went through a metamorphosis into the tremendously developed hearing, which opens upon the infinite realm of sound waves in the air and the water. The dolphin is a creature listening attentively to the world, forming its picture of existence through these perceptions. By means of the breath these tones, sounds and noises are transformed into conscious experiences, which then probably become memories.

Man alone is observed by the dolphin by means of the eye; this is evident from many of the descriptions given by Lilly and his fellow-workers. When the human individual with and through his eyes, gazes at the dolphin, it becomes tame and friendly. Does a memory then arise in it of old long-past times, when it was still itself upon the way towards humanity? At the moment of such a meeting of eyes, do pictures of its evolution dawn upon its consciousness? So that it then takes children or youths upon its back and bears them through the waves, indicating that it wished to become what they now are, and gladly acknowledges their humanity? This belongs to the visual world of the dolphin.

With hearing, it lives in the realm of nature, not of the human. In this it hunts for fish, defeats that ancestral enemy, the shark, and darts through the water. But directly seamen and fishermen appear in their ships and boats, it becomes friendly, happy and tame. Then the eye enters their consciousness, with light and air as the dominant environment.

It is as if the dolphin lives in a world divided into two; in the heights of air and light and in the depths of sound and water. In one world, which air sustains, he encounters man. In the other sphere, in which he finds his nourishment, and his living space as an animal, he encounters the other animals, which are his enemies or his companions.

Slijper (1962, 204) relates that in the Marineland Institute dolphins were frightened by sounds between 300 and 400 kilocycles (about from low C to high A).

Such observations show clearly that our hearing and that of the dolphin have an opposite background of feeling: what for us is music frightens them and drives them away; what for us is painful, like a high-pitched siren attracts them.

They are thus remote from us — and yet a part of us. But what was it that caused them to seek out, when they departed from evolution towards humanity, the ocean depths instead of the dry land?

A Greek legend tells of the younger Dionysus (Kerényi 1951):

. . . how he was carried off, when he stood on the shore looking into the distance, by Etruscan pirates. They bound him to the mast; but the bonds 'fell from his hands and feet. He sat there smiling, with dark eyes'. A mighty vine grew up about the mast and sails, and the sweet fragrance of a noble wine filled the boat and made the crew and their captain drunk. Only the helmsman remained sober and recognized that he had a god on board. But Dionysus took the form of a lion threatening the seamen; in terror they leapt into the sea and were there transformed into dolphins swimming round the boat. The helmsman alone remained free of this metamorphosis. The god was revealed to him as son of Zeus and Semele.

For the Greeks the origin of the dolphin is connected with the work of the younger Dionysus. He who cannot master the fragrance and power of wine — so they may have thought — becomes a dolphin. The one who remains conscious and upright, as the helmsman does, may remain in the realm of humanity. Rudolf Steiner once said about this Dionysus (1963, 98 [1911 Aug 22]): 'For the macro-cosmic counterpart of our present ego-consciousness, with its intellectual civilization, with all that derives from our reason, and from our ego generally, is in fact the second Dionysus' the son of Zeus and Semele. And he points to the other legend, which tells of Dionysus' journey towards Asia (1963, 99), ' . . . everywhere teaching men the arts of agriculture, the cultivation of the vine, and so on . . . Every variety of intellectual civilization stems from the journeys of the younger Dionysus . . .'

He who cannot make his step towards the consciousness of the 'I' is left behind and becomes a dolphin. This, although it is expressed in a mythological picture, is a key to the nature of the dolphin.

The human consciousness of the 'I', when it is achieved, can only develop because the brain becomes a mirror for thoughts and mental pictures. Rudolf Steiner indicates this when describing the creative powers which brought this about (1963, 120 [1911 Aug 24]):

> When the ancient Greek was directing his feeling upon the microcosm, upon man, he called this element — coming from the Earth and thus macrocosmic — this element which played a part in the constructing of the brain, the *Dionysian principle*; so that it is Dionysus who works in us to make our bodily organism into a mirror of our spiritual life.

Here the historic sacrifice of the dolphin can be clearly recognized. He throws himself down from the ship of human evolution which is led by Dionysus, into the sea. He leaves the vehicle of the developing intellect in order to take with him those forces of the depths which would otherwise prevent the body from becoming the mirror of human thought. The true children of Dionysus remain above, in the light; the powers of the depths, which the god only summons at definite times of year (at the festivals of Dionysus) remain with the whales, which once liberated humanity from them.

When the sound of the flute rang out, when Marsyas arose against Apollo and the forces which opposed Dionysus were let loose, then those powers worked, which were indicated in Greece with the word *delphos*, the 'womb'. These are the same powers which the Greek knew to be guarded by the power of Apollo at his central sanctuary, at Delphi, which bears the same name.

The foundation of this sanctuary is described by two legends, among many others; both are concerned with the dolphin. One ascribes the origin of the oracle to Eucadio, the son of Apollo. He and his companion, the nymph Lycia, were shipwrecked. In their need a dolphin came and took both upon his back, carrying them to the foot of Parnassus. There Eucadio dedicated to his divine father the sanctuary of Delphi.

But it is recorded of Apollo himself that he once took the form of a mighty dolphin which lay down upon the deck of a Cretan boat which was sailing to Greece. By his mighty presence he compelled the boat to take its course to Crissa, the harbour of Delphi. Here Apollo sprang ashore like 'a star at midday. Many shining sparks flew from him, and a glory of light reached the heavens.' But Apollo appeared to the terrified and wondering Cretans in the form of a youth, who led them to the sanctuary and consecrated them as the first priests of Delphi.

In both these myths, a dolphin led to the foundation of the oracle at Delphi. It became a special sanctuary because powers of the depths — incorporated in the Pythia, working through the priests — were there at work, though bound and mastered. Were these the same forces which were once conquered by Dionysus? Or were they still mightier forces of darkness?

An ancient legend speaks of two different dragons dwelling at the foot of Mount Parnassus: one a male named Typhon, the other female, named Delphyne. She was regarded as the greatest enemy of Apollo. In order to overcome this dragon, Apollo had to transform himself into it. This was the power that ruled over forces of nature which preside over the blind processes of self-reproduction and birth, in their continual repetitions. (For *delphos* is the womb.) From this 'dolphin' form

Apollo rises free, like a star, becoming its master. Thus through the Pythoness the otherwise unbridled reproductive powers of the feminine nature, overcome by the sungod, were able to speak. Thus the image of Apollo lives on in the consciousness of the Greeks and of later peoples as slayer of the dragon.

Rudolf Steiner described this (1963, 66 [1913 Dec 30]):
> And the Greeks imagined Apollo as shooting his arrows at the dragon, as it rose from the cleft in the form of turbulent vapours. Here, in the Greek Apollo, we see an earthly reflection of St. George, shooting his arrows at the dragon. And when Apollo had overcome the dragon, the Python, a temple was built, and instead of the dragon we see how the vapours entered the soul of the Pythia, and how the Greeks imagined that Apollo lived in these swirling dragon-vapours and prophesied to them through the oracle, through the lips of the Pythia.

Apollo had to transform himself into 'Delphyne'. In this way he won the power to conquer the Python. In its vapours his being could then work. Thus Apollo bore, among many other names that of the dolphin: Apollo Delphynios.

In connection with the form of the sun-god we meet the imagination of the dolphin in its macrocosmic being. Here are these primeval evolutionary powers which are mastered by Apollo. The dolphins which accompany the younger Dionysus represent the same forces in a human, microcosmic form. In the wide spaces of creation the light-god Apollo conquers the dark forces of the depths. Within the human soul Dionysus masters the dolphin and thus makes possible the awakening of intellectual consciousness.

The two paths of initiation which existed among the Greeks are indicated in this way. One led the pupil out into the wide spaces of Nature; the other into the depths of his own being. But at Delphi both paths were united.

In spring Apollo came from the north and dwelt for nine months at the sanctuary. In winter Dionysus replaced him. Both were guardians of the Delphic, sub-earthly powers which are at work in the turbulent being and becoming of Nature.

Here we find ourselves at the centre of the mysterious destiny of our dolphin, which we set out to seek. The mighty baleen whales appear as the result of the Apollonian, the more southern toothed whales as the result of the Dionysian, activities in the cosmos and in man.

Now we can ask about the external evolution of both families. Can anything yet be known about this? Only in recent years have decisive discoveries been made in this direction. Through serological research it has been proved that the whales are very closely related to the artiodactyls (pigs, camels, ruminants). Both great groups can be traced back hypothetically to a common ancestor in the Eocene period, that is in early Atlantis. A few specimens of this family, which must have had many branches and forms, have been found during the last hundred years or so. They are included in the animal system under the name *archaeocetes*.

They all have a dragon-like body. The limbs are atrophied, particularly the hind limbs. The bodies are of tremendous size. The nose still lies at the front and is closely connected with the mouth, as in terrestrial mammals. From this original form the ungulates as well as the whales are derived.

Should we not assume that this dragon-like mammal lived in marshes? Why otherwise would its limbs have atrophied? It waded and crawled; it could not walk. With the gradual hardening of the earth two distinct groups formed. One mounted the dry land and developed into the ungulates; the other remained in the water and developed into the whales. The whales have never been terrestrial mammals. They have passed through a metamorphosis from the dragon-like *archaeocetes* descending into rivers and seas. This came about in the course of the Atlantean age. This dragon transformation is quite a different process from that which led to the extinction of the great saurians at the end of the Lemurian period. For here a dragon — in which the lower nature of existence and of man is expressed — is metamorphosed into higher forms. The powers of light and of the sun, Apollo's deeds and sufferings, conquer him. This process of evolution appears to have reached its end towards the conclusion of the Atlantean period.

Into this period falls an event, which is described in spiritual science as the third pre-earthly deed of Christ. At this time the Christ being, working from beyond the earth, brought about a harmonizing of the three powers of the human soul; thinking, feeling and willing are brought into equilibrium. Rudolf Steiner says (1963, 64 [1913 Dec 30]):

> [The Christ being was] able to drive out from
> thinking, feeling and willing the element which
> would have raged within them as a dragon and
> brought them into chaos.
>
> A reminiscence of this is preserved in all the
> pictures of St. George vanquishing the Dragon
> which are found in the records of human culture.

The Greeks beheld their god Apollo in the same picture.

There is a wonderful consequence of the harmony brought about in this way. '. . . a weak echo of it could be heard in the musical art cultivated by the Greeks under the protection of Apollo.' (Steiner 1963, 68).

Here we meet again the picture found in many Greek myths: Arion, the singer and harpist, who returns to his home Lesbos, the place of Apollo's birth, carried by dolphins. Man receives the art of music through the sacrifice once brought by the dolphins. They took the powers of the dragon with them into the depths of the water; thereby something else was rescued.

Man's path led upward; he was accompanied by the

race of ungulates. Beneath their feet the marshy earth that they were leaving behind grew harder. Feet became hooves. The herds could appear on the firm ground of the steppes and meadows that came into being. They grew teats and became givers of milk for man and for animal. Horns and antlers sprang from their heads; new, otherwise unknown symbols of their destiny. They raised these structures, like archetypes of those musical instruments which give men the art of strings, into the atmosphere. The cythera and the lyre appeared in their perfect beauty upon their brows.

What the whales keep as a mighty brain mass within their skulls is shown here outwardly in the form of horn and antler. In man both form and mass are transformed into the power of thought. Substance and shape are spiritualized.

Thankfulness that this could happen should fill the heart of man with endless humility, when he looks at the whale and the dolphin, at the ox and the sheep and the antelope. For this reason the ox could be one of the first to greet the Child lying in the manger. The ox could be present as representative of all the ungulates and the whales of the earth, at the place of holiest poverty.

Bibliography

Alpers, Antony. 1960. *A Book of Dolphins*. London: Murray.
Aristotle. *Historia Animalium. History of the Animals*.
Banse, Ewald. 1932. *Geographische Landschaftskunde*. Gotha: Perthes.
Brehm, Alfred. 1911. *Vögel*. (Vol. 6 of *Tierleben*). Leipzig: Bibliogr. Institut.
——1914, *Die Fische*, (Vol. 3 of *Tierleben*). Leipzig: Bibliogr. Institut.
Evans, *see* Muir-Evans, Harold.
Frazer, James George. 1911. *The Golden Bough*. London: Macmillan.
Gerlach, Richard. 1950. *Die Fische*. Hamburg: Claassen.
——1964. *Die Gefiederten. Das schöne Leben der Vögel*. München & Zürich: Droemersche.
Hermann, Ernst. 1959. *Die Pole der Erde*. Berlin: Safari.
Kearton, Cherry. 1930. *The Island of Penguins*. London: Longman Green.
Kerényi, Karl. 1951. *Die Mythologie der Griechen*. Zürich: Rhein.
Kraus, Eugen. 1932. *Das Aalproblem der modernen Biologie*. Dornach: Goetheanum.
Lilly, John C. 1962. *Man and Dolphin*. London: Gollancz.
Lockley, Ronald Mathias. 1954. *The Seals and the Curragh*. London: Dent.
Lucanus, Friedrich von. 1929. *Zugvögel und Vogelzug*. Berlin: J. Springer.
Marret, Mario. 1956. *Sieben Mann bei den Pinguinen*. Bern: Kümmerley & Frey.
Muir-Evans, Harold. 1943. *Sting-fish and Seafarer*. London: Faber.
Norris, Kenneth S., John H. Prescott, Paul V. Asa-Dorian, and Paul Perkins. 1961, April. 'An Experimental Demonstration of Echo-Location Behaviour in the Porpoise, *Tursiops truncatus.' Biological Bulletin*. Woods Hole, Mass.: Marine Biology Laboratory.
Portmann, Adolf. 1957. *Von Vögeln und Insekten*. Basel: Rheinhadt.
Rabinovitch, Melitta. 1947. *Der Delphin in Sage und Mythos der Griechen*. Dornach: Hybernia.
Rivolier, Jean. 1956. *Emperor Penguins*. London: Elek.
Roule, Louis. 1933. *Fishes, their Journeys and Migrations*. London: Routledge.
Scheffer, Victor Blanchard. 1958. *Seals, Sea Lions and Walruses*. Stanford: Stanford University Press.

BIBLIOGRAPHY

Slijpers, Everhard Johannes. 1958. *Walvissen*. Amsterdam: Centen.
——1962. *Whales*. London: Hutchinson.
Steiner, Rudolf. 1952 [1924]. *Cosmic Workings in Earth and Man*. London: Steiner.
——1955 [1908]. *Universe, Earth and Man*. London: Steiner.
——1959 [1908]. *Cosmic Memory*. Englewood, New Jersey: Steiner.
——1963 [1911]. *Wonders of the World, Ordeals of the Soul, Revelations of the Spirit*. London: Steiner.
——1963 [1913/14]. *Christ and the Spiritual World*. London: Steiner.
——1967 [1921]. *Menschenwerden, Weltenseele und Weltengeist*, Vol. 1. (Gesamtausgabe (GA) No. 205). Dornach: Steiner.
——1970 [1910]. *The Mission of Folk-Souls*. London: Steiner.
——1970 [1923]. *Man as Symphony of the Creative Word*. London: Steiner.
——1971 [1908]. *Egyptian Myths and Mysteries*. New York: Anthroposophic.
——1973 [1908]. *Aus der Akascha-Chronik*. (GA 11). Dornach: Steiner.
——1977 [1911]. *Weltenwunder, Seelenprüfung und Geistesoffenbarung*. (GA 129) Dornach: Steiner.
——1977 [1913/14]. *Christus und die geistige Welt. Von der Suche nach dem heiligen Gral*. (GA 149). Dornach: Steiner.
——1978 [1908]. *Ägyptische Mythen und Mysterien*. (GA 106). Dornach: Steiner.
——1978 [1923]. *Der Mensch als Zusammenklang des schaffenden, bildenden und gestaltenden Weltenwortes*. (GA 230). Dornach: Steiner.
——1981 [1917]. *Geisteswissenschaftliche Erläuterung zu Goethes Faust*, Vol. 2. (GA 273). Dornach: Steiner.
——1981 [1920]. *Grenzen der Naturerkenntnis*. (GA 322). Dornach: Steiner.
——1981 [1924]. *Natur und Mensch in geisteswissenschaftlicher Betrachtung*. (GA 352). Dornach: Steiner.
——1982 [1910]. *Die Mission einzelner Volkseelen im Zusammenhang mit der germanisch-nordischen Mythologie*. (GA 121). Dornach: Steiner.
——1983 [1908]. *Welt, Erde und Mensch*. (GA 105). Dornach: Steiner.
——1983 [1920]. *The Boundaries of Natural Science*. Spring Valley, New York: Anthroposophical.
Tier, Das. 1964. Bern: Hallwag.
Urner, Hildegarde. 1959. 'Der Delphin als religions- und kunstgeschichtliches Motiv'. *Neue Zürcher Zeitung*, Oct 3. Zürich.
Wachsmuth, Günther. 1950. *Die Entwickelung der Erde*. Dornach: Philosophisch-Anthroposophischer.

Swans and Storks
Doves and Sparrows

Karl König

The second part of König's sketches for an imaginative zoology.

Publication: 1985

Elephants
Bears, horses, cats and dogs

Karl König

The final part of König's sketches for an imaginative zoology.

Publication about 1986

Floris Books

The First Three Years of the Child

Karl König

The author examines the first three years of the life of the child in the light of the three major achievements that dominate them: learning to walk, speak and think.

Brothers and Sister

The order of birth in the family

Karl König

The fact of being a first, second or third child determines how we approach life and its demands.

Floris Books

Scientist of the Invisible

An introduction of the life and work of Rudolf Steiner

A P Shepherd

Foreword by Owen Barfield

Written in 1954 to counter widespread lack of knowledge about Steiner, the first part of the book is biographical and the second part penetrates deeply into his work.

Rudolf Steiner Enters My Life

Friedrich Rittelmeyer

Rittelmeyer writes of his many conversations with one of the most important figures of our time. He chronicles his ten years of apprehension, critical investigation and cautious scrutiny of the new body of thought.

Floris Books